"Your Room?"

He laughed, a low, deep chuckle filled with mockery. "So that's going to be your story."

"It's the truth! You know it is!"

He was staring at her, and suddenly, she was afraid of him again. The silence was more threatening than his words. There was a strange urgency in his black gaze drifting slowly over her. Then his hand moved to her throat, down to her slender shoulders. His touch was oddly gentle, sensual, expert. When he lowered his lips to hers and kissed her in a slow, deliberate way, it took away her breath.

ANN MAJOR

is not only a successful author; she also manages a business and runs a busy household with three small children. Among her many interests she lists traveling and playing the piano—her favorite composer, quite naturally, the romantic Chopin.

Dear Reader:

During the last year, many of you have written to Silhouette telling us what you like best about Silhouette Romances and, more recently, about Silhouette Special Editions. You've also told us what else you'd like to read from Silhouette. With your comments and suggestions in mind, we've developed SILHOUETTE DESIRE.

SILHOUETTE DESIREs will be on sale this June, and each month we'll bring you four new DESIREs written by some of your favorite authors—Stephanie James, Diana Palmer, Rita Clay, Suzanne Simms and many more.

SILHOUETTE DESIREs may not be for everyone, but they are for those readers who want a more sensual, provocative romance. The heroines are slightly older—women who are actively involved in their careers and the world around them. If you want to experience all the excitement, passion and joy of falling in love, then SILHOUETTE DESIRE is for you.

I'd appreciate any thoughts you'd like to share with us on new SILHOUETTE DESIRE, and I invite you to write to us at the address below:

Karen Solem
Editor-in-Chief
Silhouette Books
P.O. Box 769
New York, N.Y. 10019

ANN MAJOR

A Touch of Fire

Silhouette Romance

Published by Silhouette Books New York

America's Publisher of Contemporary Romance

Other Silhouette Books by Ann Major

Wild Lady

SILHOUETTE BOOKS, a Simon & Schuster Division of
GULF & WESTERN CORPORATION
1230 Avenue of the Americas, New York, N.Y. 10020

ISBN: 0-671-57150-8

First Silhouette Books printing May, 1982

10 9 8 7 6 5 4 3 2 1

America's Publisher of Contemporary Romance

Printed in the U.S.A.

For Leta Major,
a grand lady,
who's been a constant inspiration
in my life.

Chapter One

"Where is Gary, anyway?" Helen Freeman asked half-aloud as she zipped herself into an evening gown that was yards and yards of apricot chiffon sprinkled with flashing sequins. The filmy material drifted over her slender curves and swirled gracefully like flowing fire as she moved about her hotel suite. The dress was far more glamorous than the rest of her wardrobe. It had been a gift for one of her recitals from Hal, her father, who, as usual, had been too busy to attend.

She paused before the ornate gilt mirror and ran her brush one last time through the rippling waves of honey-gold hair that fell almost to her waist. She set the brush down and twisted her wrist slightly so that she could better view the band of gold and tiny diamonds that was her watch.

He was ten minutes late; if he didn't come soon, the tour bus would leave without them.

She sighed with impatience. Traveling through Europe with her teen-aged brother, Gary, had proved to be rather more of an ordeal than she'd expected.

Were all sixteen-year-olds such free spirits? Gary—carefree and indolently good-natured—drifted through the days without any regard for punctuality. He was driving their tour director mad and straining her own patience.

When she'd picked Gary up at his Swiss boarding school, it had taken her a full minute to realize that the tall, long-haired youth with the warm, familiar smile and the perpetual slouch was Gary. He, as well as his untidy blond hair, seemed to have grown six inches since she'd seen him at Christmas. Fortunately, he'd allowed her to persuade him that a hair trim was in order.

Where was he?

She started toward the French doors that opened onto the balcony that looked out onto a Paris veiled with lavender skies. She was halfway across the vast suite when a knock sounded at her door. She turned briskly and crossed the room to answer it.

"Gary . . ." She spoke his name in shock as her blue eyes, thickly fringed with brown lashes, went over his unkempt form. "You can't possibly go to the ballet dressed like . . . like that."

He was wearing a sweatshirt and jeans that were splattered with black grease.

"I'm going to change," he agreed lazily. He stepped into her room as if he had all the time in the world. He almost succeeded in disarming her with an affectionate smile.

"Gary, do you realize what time it is?"

"Simmer down. I was helping Poros change a flat on our bus. We wouldn't be going anywhere if I hadn't given him a hand."

Sisterly annoyance drained away. Gary's mechanical knowhow had come in handy more than once when their bus had broken down for minor repairs in the Swiss Alps. Gary meant well; it was impossible to stay angry with him for long.

8

Gary was staring at her room with amazement. "This is really nice! How'd you rate something so fancy when the rest of us are squeezed into matchbox-sized rooms on the sixth floor? And what's this?"

His long fingers moved lazily over the strange design that was emblazoned on everything in the room. It was an abstract design which resembled a bird with wings of fire. It was on the bedspread, the headboard, the doorknobs.

"I don't know," she replied, glancing around the lavishly decorated hotel suite. "But I don't suppose it's too unusual. This is one of the most famous hotels in Europe."

She really hadn't had a chance to give the room too much thought. She'd scarcely been in it fifteen minutes since she'd checked in. She'd spent the day on a motorcoach tour taking in such landmarks as the Louvre, the Opéra, the Notre-Dame cathedral, the Latin Quarter, and the Champs-Elysées. When she'd returned, she'd unpacked, bathed, and begun dressing for the ballet.

Ornate chandeliers swung from ceilings carved in deep relief. Draperies which cascaded over the long windows were made of fine silk. Plush Oriental carpets stretched across polished marble floors. Never had she seen anything more fabulous. She reminded herself again that this was one of the oldest and finest hotels in Paris. Sometimes when hotels were almost full, they were forced to put guests in some of their finer suites.

Gary had moved across the room and was standing beneath an enormous oil painting. A brilliant, fiery bird flamed across the canvas. The title of the painting was written beneath it on the ornate golden frame: *L'Oiseau de Feu.*

"The firebird," he translated. "Isn't that the name of the ballet you're making me take you to tonight?"

"As a matter of fact, it is," she answered, ignoring the startling coincidence, "which brings us back to you and the way you look."

"I can't get over this place," he was saying, not paying any attention to what she said. "Looks like something a king would live in."

"Well, it doesn't matter," she said firmly. "What matters is you and the way you're dressed."

"All right. All right."

She walked with Gary down to his room and waited while he showered and changed into a sport jacket and slacks.

When they arrived downstairs, the tour bus was full, and although Poros, the driver and mechanic, beamed at them, the tour director, a rigid little man, was scowling impatiently as he twisted the knob of his watch.

"The Freemans at last," he said sarcastically, stepping onto the bus after them and pulling the doors shut. The scowl disappeared from the little Greek's face as his black eyes followed Helen as she moved gracefully down the aisle looking for a seat. Then she found one, and, slipping into it, she disappeared from his view. The tour director sat down himself. The big engine of the bus roared as Poros pulled out into the traffic and headed toward the place Vendôme and then down the famed rue de la Paix. The tour director's voice was a steady drone into his microphone as he pointed out the sights along the way to the elegant restaurant where they were to dine.

It was late—at least three A.M.—when Helen, dangling glittering high heels in one hand, padded down the long, thickly carpeted corridor to her suite. Her chiffon gown flowed around her like a filmy flame.

The ballet had been marvelous; she'd thoroughly

enjoyed the Russian ballerina who'd danced the part of the firebird with an almost savage passion. Dreamily, she remembered the first scene of the ballet: the dazzling dance of the firebird, her capture by Prince Ivan, her frantic struggle to free herself, her pitiful begging that he have mercy. Finally, Prince Ivan, moved to pity for his fiery captive, had gently released her, and the firebird repaid him for his kindness with a magic feather. Helen had been deeply touched by the performance; her brother had been painfully bored. Gary had been interested only when one of the flaming torches the firebird whirled had set a piece of scenery on fire and stagehands had scrambled to put it out.

Now Helen's feet were aching both from dancing and from the long walk back to the hotel. She had a headache, as well. The Mortimers had insisted on walking home so they could window-shop along the rue du Faubourg St. Honoré and the boulevard des Capucines.

Helen, whose temples throbbed, was almost limp with exhaustion as she at last reached the door to her suite. She fumbled in her purse for the key.

As soon as she stepped into the foyer, she was aware of a difference in the suite. Apprehension traced tingling fingers down her spine. She had the strangest feeling that she was not alone.

There was a heady fragrance of freshly cut flowers. Someone had come in since she'd gone out, she told herself. The maid . . . no doubt . . . There couldn't be anyone here . . . now.

She flipped on the light just to reassure herself, and then just as quickly flipped it off again—feeling much more secure. It had been painfully bright. She rubbed her forehead where it hurt. Her eyes grew accustomed to the dimness of the suite.

Slowly, she groped her way across the foyer and

through a sitting room to the bedroom. She stopped hesitantly before the king-sized bed and debated for a fleeting instant the advantages of going to the bathroom, removing her makeup, and preparing herself properly for bed. She rejected the idea quickly; she was too exhausted.

Moonlight was flooding through the partially opened draperies, bathing her with its silvery brilliance. The sequins of her gown caught the light and sparkled like fire. Only the part of the room where she stood was lighted; the rest, including the bed, was shrouded in shadows. Again for no reason at all her neck prickled with anxiety.

Slowly, she unzipped her chiffon gown; it fell like a shower of flame over her breasts, her narrow waist, and her hips to the floor. She stooped gracefully and picked it up, placing it on the chair by the bed. Then she pulled her stockings slowly over the delicate curves of her legs and removed them, draping them over the back of the chair. It never occurred to her that her every movement was seductive, for she thought herself to be alone.

She sank down onto the bed. She wore only her full slip, which was wrought of sheer, delicate—almost transparent—apricot lace. Then she slipped into bed, pulling the satin sheets and coverlets around her. The bed was blissfully soft. She stretched languidly, curling her body into a comfortable position. She would have fallen into an immediate and deep sleep had not a movement nearby startled her into a state of stunned shock.

Bedsheets rustled and she felt the heavy movements of someone on the far side of the bed.

She was not alone! Fear charged through her rigid body like a high-voltage current. Then the bedside lamp flashed on—brilliant and blinding. In reflex, she squeezed her eyes tightly shut and fought against the impulse to scream.

This couldn't be happening! She was dreaming! When she opened her eyes and found herself truly awake, she would be alone.

Slowly, she opened her eyes and stared with a lingering sense of unreality across the bed at the man beside her.

She blinked once and then again, and when he did not disappear she knew he was every bit as real as she was. She drew in a sharp, quick gasp.

The man's black eyes roved over her, down the slender column that was her throat, over her breasts heaving beneath transparent lace. His gaze was too knowing, and her heart began to pound like the rapid thudding of a trip-hammer.

There was a startled wild light in her blue eyes, a questioning fear on her incredibly beautiful face. Her hair was waves of fire tumbling over her shoulders.

His lips, full and sensual, parted in a cynical half-smile as though her appearance, at least, did not displease him. Something about her, however, did displease him, for the smile quickly vanished and his brows creased together.

For a timeless moment neither of them spoke. Each seemed to assess the other.

She glared fearfully at him, determined to memorize his features in case he turned out to be some sort of criminal.

His virile handsomeness was an attractive blending of rugged features. His hair was black and faintly curled, his skin bronzed as a pirate's. The upper half of his body, disturbingly exposed because he was sitting up and the sheets had fallen to his waist, was lean and hard with muscle. His eyes were so dark they appeared almost black. They were lustrous and blazed from beneath thick, splashing brows with some dark emotion she did not understand. His nose was long and curved slightly; he had a strong, hard jawline.

Strangely, had she passed him on the street she would never have thought him a criminal, for she always thought criminals had some innate weakness in their characters that drove them to crime. Everything about this man seemed strong and hard. Somehow, he did not look to be the kind of man who would slip into a woman's bedroom in the dead of night with the thought of molesting her. Helen could not imagine him . . . Well, perhaps after tonight she would have to revise her notions about criminals.

The tense silence came to an abrupt end. Staring fiercely at her with a possessive arrogance she found degrading, he moved toward her. A scream bubbled to her lips, and quickly his hand covered her mouth. Suddenly, she was pulled against his steel-hard chest.

"No screams tonight, little one," he said in deep, vibrant tones that fell pleasantly to her ears. He spoke French, which she understood because of the long, lonely years she'd spent in Swiss boarding schools.

She was captured in his strong arms and held closely to him. She felt the long sweep of his body against her own, the rush of his heartbeat as her ear nestled against his warm chest.

She knew she should fight him, but he would only subdue her with his greater strength. She found that prospect humiliating, so she continued to lie still, beneath him. Better passive resistance than to fight wildly, only to be defeated in the end. She wouldn't give him that satisfaction. Still he continued to stare down at her as if he owned her; she thought his gaze stripped away apricot lace, as his hands would doubtless do before too much more time elapsed.

"I see you are afraid of me, as you deserve to be," he said. His accent was heavy, and it was not French. She moved her mouth in response, but as his hand covered the lower part of her face, no sound came out.

"You would speak?" he continued. She nodded. "If you try to scream, I'll . . ." She flinched at the savage fire in his eyes, at the hoarse anger she heard in his voice.

He removed his hand and she lay silently beneath him trying to gather her courage so that her voice wouldn't tremble.

"H-how did you get in here? W-what are you planning . . . ?" Her quavering voice trailed off. It was difficult to speak French when she was so terrified.

"Ah, you're American," he said in almost perfect English. His enunciation was somehow foreign, but she couldn't place his accent.

"Yes. But, w-who are you? What are you doing here?" she asked.

"You are asking me the questions you yourself should be answering."

"W-what?"

"What are you doing in *my* suite? How did you get in here?"

"I . . . I . . ."

"What is your cheap little scheme?" he demanded. When she only stared up at him in amazement, he asked, "Are you from one of the scandal sheets?"

"No. Of course not!" Her voice was scarcely more than a whisper.

"Then one of my enemies employed you!" he stated emphatically. "Are your friends waiting outside for the proper interval of time to elapse for us to be discovered in . . . compromising circumstances?" Her eyes widened. "Will they burst through the door with their cameras clicking and their flash bulbs blazing in a matter of seconds? Do you intend blackmail?" When she still said nothing, his hand went to her throat in what was almost a caress. "Or is this your own little scheme?"

Where his calloused thumb stroked her flesh, her skin tingled.

There was an overpowering quality about him—something that was rawly vital, unsettlingly male.

"I-I don't know what you're talking about."

"You must've bribed some clerk for the key. What do you want? Money? You thought if you slipped into my room, tantalized me with that delightful striptease, and then seduced me, I would be so taken in by your charms, I would . . ."

So—he'd actually watched her undress! He'd called it a "delightful striptease"! He spoke contemptuously to her, as if he thought no more of her than he would a woman he could hire for his pleasure. She felt warmth like an angry flood wash over her. Futilely, she hoped he didn't see her embarrassment. He had sneaked into her room, and he had the gall to accuse her! And of such disgusting things! Was he a madman? She remembered his ugly accusations anew, and fury flamed through her and tinged her cheeks with its fire. Her blue eyes sparked.

"I did no such thing! This is *my* room! Not yours! As you well know!"

"Your room?" He laughed—a low, deep chuckle that seemed filled with mockery. "So that's going to be your story."

"It's the truth!" When he laughed harshly again, she said, "You know it is!"

He was staring at her hard. Indeed, every part of him seemed hard, and suddenly she was afraid of him again. After a long time, he said, "You think you can pull any trick, however low, and get away with it, don't you?

And all because you've the face of an angel, the big blue eyes of an innocent. If you'd come to me and knocked on my door and asked me for whatever it is you so desperately need, I would have given it to you. But no, you had to be devious and trick some poor desk clerk into giving you the key, and he'll probably be sacked as a result. And now . . . I think it's time someone taught you a lesson. This is one night you're going to get exactly what you deserve. You came in here intending to use me, but it is I who will use you."

His voice stopped and the silence that followed his words was more threatening even than his words had been. There was a strange urgency in his black gaze as his eyes drifted slowly over her—ravishing her. His brown hand moved from her throat over her slender shoulder to the narrow strip of lace that was the strap of her slip. He caught it in his fingers; slowly, he pushed it downward. His touch was oddly gentle—deeply sensual, expert.

Her eyes widened in horror. "N-no! No! Don't!" She would have screamed, but he lowered his lips to hers and kissed her in a slow, deliberate manner which took her breath away. She opened her mouth slightly, as if to obey the silent command of his lips, and she felt his tongue enter and probe.

A wild panic went through her. Even though rationally she realized to fight him would prove futile, she tried to push him away from her. He only took advantage of her struggles and molded her body to his. But as his mouth completed the punishing possession of hers, the vengeful anger that had driven him to the action dissolved. Although he held her firmly, the lingering touch of his lips on hers gentled.

Slowly, he withdrew his lips from hers; he released her. His slashing brows drew together in a quizzical frown as he studied her.

Suddenly, beneath his unwavering gaze she burst into tears as her shock and shame combined. No one . . . ever . . . had thought her to be the kind of woman he obviously believed her to be. No one had ever treated her in such a way.

She knew he was still looking at her, but his puzzled face was no more than a dark blur through her tears.

"Stop crying," he commanded sternly.

"I-I can't." Her whole body was trembling; she was quivering with hysteria, gasping deeply in an effort to breathe.

"You deserved such treatment after . . ."

"I-I-I didn't," was all she could manage.

There was a long, tense silence broken only by her own ragged gasps.

Slowly, his arm slipped beneath her and he pulled her to him so that her face rested on his tan shoulder. Still weeping, she trembled against him.

He muttered an oath to himself. "What made me . . ." He tightened his grip on her arm. "There . . . there, little one," he soothed in deep, melodious tones, pulling her closer. "I'm not going to hurt you. I promise." Gently, he brushed her hair back from her face.

They lay together, she sobbing quietly and he holding her. Slowly, her fear of him drained away and her tears stopped. Strangely, she found his presence as comforting as she'd found it menacing only minutes before.

"Feeling better?" he asked at last.

"Yes."

She moved her head from his shoulder, and it sank into the depths of the satin pillow beside him. She was still facing him. He scarcely noticed that she'd moved away. He seemed lost in thought as he stared upward into the shadows at the ornate chandelier that hung from the ceiling. She was glad of the chance to study his features without him observing that she did so.

His black hair tumbled over his high dark brows. He had a long, slightly curving nose, full, sensual lips, and a strong jawline. For the first time she saw the scar that curled like a purple ribbon from his earlobe down his neck over his shoulder. She saw that a heavy gold medallion hung from his neck. Her eyes fastened on the strange design of the medallion. It was a bird with wings of fire. It was the design that was on everything in the room.

This was his room!

He turned toward her and she was terribly aware of his virile handsomeness. When his eyes met hers with an intense look that left her breathless, she colored deeply. This man was a stranger, and she was in bed with him as though he were her intimate. As he continued to stare at her in that boldly assessing way he had, her color heightened and she tried to look away. He caught her chin with his hand. There was a puzzled glint in his eyes.

"Don't try to look away. I want to see into your eyes."

"All right," she replied meekly, not daring to cross him.

"You've never had anything like this happen before, have you?" he asked grimly.

"No."

"Have you ever been with any man as you are now with me—in bed?"

She went crimson, and tried to look away from him. But he held her chin tightly in his fingers. She had no idea how bewitchingly innocent she appeared to him with her eyes over-large, her cheeks flushed, and her hair flowing like a fiery cloud about her.

"How old are you?" he demanded.

"Twenty-two."

"For an American, you're rather old to be a virgin."

She went an even deeper shade of red with embarrassment. No man—let alone a stranger—had ever talked to her as he was talking to her.

"It's obvious you know nothing of the nature of men, or you would never have done something as stupid as you just did," he continued. "I can see you've suffered a severe shock. I only hope you've learned your lesson. If you're wise you won't try something like this again. Another man might not have my gallant nature."

"Gallant nature . . . You . . . you . . ."

"All I did was kiss you, and now I'm perfectly willing to let you go without pressing any charges against you—if you'll tell me the truth. What did you hope to gain by this little trick of yours?"

"I-I promise I wasn't tricking you. I'm beginning to think the hotel must have made some sort of mistake and assigned both of us to the same room."

"I find that difficult to believe, little one. I have been leasing this suite for the past five years. The hotel is not supposed to rent this apartment to anyone, and nothing like this has ever happened in the past."

"Please . . . you must believe me. I'm not the sort of woman who would do any of those things you accused me of. I thought you were a criminal who intended to assault me!" When his black eyes widened with incredulity that anyone could think him a criminal, Helen said, "Truly, I did! I'm touring Europe with my brother. Everyone else on our tour is on the sixth floor, but for some reason I was given this suite, on the ninth floor."

"You didn't think this rather too elaborate for the ordinary hotel suite?"

20

"I did think it was elaborate—especially after Gary pointed it out."

"Who's Gary?" His voice sounded almost angry again; his black gaze locked with hers.

"My brother . . . You see, I really didn't spend much time here. I went on one of those motorcoach tours. . . . Please, you must believe me. . . ." Her voice was tinged with desperation.

"I believe you," he said at last, releasing her chin. "I want you to get dressed while I telephone the *concierge.*"

"Please . . . don't get some poor desk clerk fired."

"What? After what just happened between us, you're worried about the fool who caused it?"

"He may have a family and needs."

"Such an imbecile shouldn't be allowed to work!" he interrupted harshly, lifting the receiver at once.

"*Le concierge, s'il vous plaît,*" he said in deep, cold tones. "I don't care if he's in bed at this hour! Get him! This is Alexander Marianatos, and I want to speak to him . . . immediately!"

She slipped from the bed and was aware of his black gaze following her as if he were mesmerized by her lovely form as she scampered with her chiffon dress toward the dressing room. When she returned, her slender curves again swathed in flaming chiffon, he was dressed himself and sitting on the edge of the vast bed, which he'd neatly made up.

He wore a scarlet blazer over a dove-colored turtleneck and slacks that were of such fine cloth and expert fit she knew they had to be crafted by his own tailor. The flamboyant color of his coat contrasted with his dark good looks, and made his hair seem nearly blue-black in the dim light.

At the sight of him so devastatingly attractive, so totally male, her heartbeats skipped crazily.

21

"The *concierge* and I have just had a long talk," he began. "Sit down, and I will explain what happened." He indicated by a wave of his brown hand the chair she'd laid her clothes on earlier. "A Mademoiselle Helen Freeman from a U.S. tour group was assigned room 609. I assume you are Helen Freeman?" She nodded. "As I was expected, my key was out on the desk—room number 906. The girl at the desk must have inadvertently handed you the wrong key. When my key was discovered missing and I was given a duplicate, it never occurred to anyone at the desk that you had it."

"And I didn't notice the mistake," she finished, "because our tour director registered for us and I didn't realize what my correct room number was. I just told the bellboy the room number from the key, and he took my bags up."

"Where are they now? Why didn't I see them when I came in?"

"I left them in the other room. . . ."

"Which I never use unless I'm entertaining."

"Now that everything is explained satisfactorily, I should take my bags and go down to my own room. I'm sure you're tired . . . as I am."

"I've never felt less tired," he contradicted. "And you can't go until the *concierge* comes with your key. Then I'll personally escort you and your luggage to your room."

"That won't be necessary."

"I insist."

She made no answer. She felt awkward conversing with him as if nothing out of the ordinary had occurred between them. Nervously, she twisted the folds of her chiffon gown. What was taking the *concierge* so long?

"How long will you be in Paris, Helen?"

"Helen." How strange her name sounded when he

spoke it. How her pulse leaped at the sound of it on his lips.

"Tomorrow we leave for Greece," she replied succinctly, glad that after the *concierge* arrived there would be no chance of her ever encountering this arrogant stranger again.

"And how long will you be staying in Greece?" he asked. It was obvious that he was enjoying this conversation that she could scarcely endure.

"A week." She deliberately gave the briefest answer possible, hoping to discourage further questions.

"What part of Greece?" he persisted. "The islands, or the mainland?"

"I can't imagine that you're interested in my tour of Europe," she said impatiently.

"Oh, but I am," he returned blandly, unperturbed by her own growing annoyance. "Very interested. What part of Greece?"

"Athens." She snapped off the word.

Again he chose to ignore her rising temper. "Ah. Then, after all, I will have a chance to make amends for what happened tonight. You see, I am Greek. Athens is my home. I'm only in Paris for the weekend. Natasha Chernitzky, a friend of mind, is dancing in *The Firebird*, and I'm throwing a party for her here tomorrow night."

"Mr.—I didn't catch your name."

"My name is Alexander Marianatos. You may call me Alex. It is a nickname my English friends use."

She avoided his given name for obvious reasons, but it lingered in her mind.

"Mr. Marianatos, you have nothing to make amends for. What happened was an unfortunate accident. There is absolutely no reason for us to ever see one another again."

"It's obvious you have no wish to see me again." Her

prolonged silence was tacit agreement. "Helen, you're making much too much of what happened earlier. No harm was done."

"No harm . . ." Again at the sound of her name on his lips, she was aware of a tingling sensation rippling through her. This involuntary response jarred every nerve ending in her body, but she sought composure.

"You should try to understand this from my point of view. I am an extremely wealthy man. There are people—women—who would do anything to get close to a man like me. Certain articles have been written about me in the newspapers that would make people who do not know me think I am highly susceptible where beautiful women are concerned. When you came into my room and undressed in the moonlight . . ."

His eyes rover over her curves with remembered knowledge, and her blood became roaring fire licking through her arteries. How could he even speak of having witnessed her undressing? Didn't he realize how he embarrassed her by doing that?

"I am not such a woman," she said, blushing deeply, and hating herself for doing so.

"I know that—now," he said quietly, "And I want to see you again. It's very important to me."

"But I don't want to see you," she said truthfully, rising. Desperate to escape him, she went to the door. "Please tell the *concierge* I will be waiting for him outside my room," she finished in a voice that was strangely tight and breathless.

Alexander came swiftly to stand beside her, towering masterfully over her, making her feel diminutive beside him. He caught her hand in his, and his touch was fire. She tried to draw away, but he held her tightly.

"Helen, all I did was kiss you," he said with a calmness she envied. "Surely you have been kissed by a man before."

"N-no." There was a rush of sound pounding in her temples. Why wouldn't he release her? Couldn't he see that she longed for nothing more than the safety of her own room?

He was staring at her intently, cocking one dark eyebrow with amazement. He saw that she was telling him the truth.

"You are very beautiful. Surely you must have had a boyfriend?"

She shook her head in denial, tugging at the hand he refused to relinquish. "Please, Mr. Marianatos, don't ask me these questions."

Suddenly, he understood that somehow he'd touched a deep hurt. He released her hand and she drew back. Slowly, he opened the door for her, and she fled down the corridor, her chiffon gown spreading behind her like wings of fire.

Her scarf fell from her shoulders onto the carpet, but she did not notice. When he called after her, she only quickened her flight. He stepped out into the hall and retrieved the glittering fragment. It was scented with her perfume—sweet and delicate, like the woman herself. "So tonight, like Prince Ivan in Natasha's ballet," he murmured, pocketing the scarf as he closed the door behind him, "I captured my own firebird and set her free—for a while."

Chapter Two

Helen scarcely slept after she left Alexander. Instead, she lay awake—thinking of him. Finally, she gave up attempting to rest and arose early—before dawn.

What she needed was a cold shower—the very thing to put that infuriating man from her mind.

She pulled her long flannel nightgown over the contours of her body and tossed it toward her suitcase. Then she stepped into the bathroom, turned on the shower, and stepped under the spray. The frigid shower was a jolt to her system—the water a driving rain of icy needles pricking her. She scrubbed her skin with a vengeance, as if to rid herself of the remembrance of Alexander's flesh against hers, of his lips possessing hers. She could almost feel the imprint of his hard muscles on her body, the powerful length of him pressing against her. Suddenly a horrible self-truth struck her: some traitorous part of her had actually enjoyed the sensation of being in bed with him, of him kissing her as if it were his right.

A second part of her mind screamed unconvincingly that it wasn't true—that she hated him!

Unaware that she'd left the shower on and that soap bubbles still clung to her body, she stepped from the shower and wrapped herself in a towel. How could her senses respond to a man she disliked so intensely? And why did she keep thinking of him?

The sound of the shower intruded into her thoughts, and she turned it off.

She dressed carefully in an ivory-colored, old-fashioned blouse and a dark brown skirt. The blouse was long-sleeved and had a high, lace collar she buttoned at her throat. When she finished dressing, she observed her reflection with dissatisfaction. She'd never noticed before how schoolgirlish the blouse was, how primly innocent she appeared in it. Suddenly, she was wondering what Alexander would think of her if he saw her, now, as she normally dressed.

He would never look twice at her under ordinary circumstances, she decided. For some idiotic reason that thought vaguely depressed her. He would want a woman who was elegant and fashionably gowned, rather than the brown-wren type.

When she finished dressing in preparation for the flight to Athens, she packed her suitcases, which the *concierge* had personally delivered.

She found herself wondering about Alexander again. What kind of man was he? How did he live? What did he think of her? Did he really intend to call her when he reached Athens? At the thought of it, a pulse jumped in her throat.

She pushed the disturbing possibility from her mind. Of course he had no intention of calling her. He would forget all about her—just as she would forget all about him. He probably already had.

She caught her breath painfully. What was she doing thinking of him and wondering about how he felt about

27

her? He was horrible! Hadn't he proved that by his behavior last night?

Resolving for the hundredth time that morning never to think of Alexander again, she went down for her Continental breakfast as soon as the hotel dining room opened. She was enjoying a croissant and a cup of black coffee when the maître d' presented her with a Paris newspaper. She opened the paper, and to her astonishment, the boldly smiling photograph of Alexander Marianatos mocked her. Just the sight of those dark, terribly male features, and her pulse was quickening. There was a lengthy article beneath the photograph. The thing to do, obviously, was to turn the page and read something of *real* interest to her. But that rebel part of herself that was drawn to the man began to devour the article.

Slowly, she read the French as if she did not want to miss a single word. She learned he was a banker as well as a shipping magnate, and that he traded heavily in the London gold market. Most of the article dealt with his relationship with Natasha Chernitzky. Helen found herself rather too fascinated by the romanticized account of the famed ballerina's defection from a U.S.S.R. resort on the Black Sea. The night she'd escaped, his yacht had been in the vicinity. The implication was clear—he'd helped her defect because he had much more than a casual interest in the dancer.

Helen remembered his words: "Certain articles have been written about me . . . that would make people . . . think I am highly susceptible where beautiful women are concerned. . . ."

She was bending her red-gold head of hair closely over the newspaper, tracing a line of French script with a manicured fingertip and totally absorbed in the account of Alexander's relationship with the tempestuous Russian, when suddenly the deep tones of an all-too-familiar voice startled her, affecting her senses as no other voice ever had.

"I'm rather surprised . . . after last night . . . to find you poring over an article about me," Alexander said smoothly. "You gave me the impression you were not interested . . . in me. I suppose I should be flattered," he continued with alarming perception.

With trembling fingers she carefully folded the newspaper and set it beside her cup of coffee. She caught her breath sharply, but that was only—she told herself frantically—because his presence was unexpected and acutely embarrassing to her.

"Good morning, Mr. Marianatos," she replied civilly, meeting his disconcerting black gaze for the briefest instant before she looked quickly away. "For your information, I read the newspaper every morning."

"Do you?" His dark brow furrowed mockingly. "A commendable habit. And do you always read it with such undivided attention?" He smiled warmly down at her, his full lips parting, revealing his gleaming white teeth.

He lifted the newspaper from the table, flicked it so that it unfolded, and scanned the article about himself.

His long black lashes were lowered as he read, and she could observe him without his knowledge that she did so. He was taller than she remembered. His broad shoulders tapered to a slim waist and hips. He was dressed in a dark green, three-piece suit that was immaculate and flawlessly cut to fit the powerful lines of his body. His silk shirt was a paler shade of green. In spite of his elegant attire, an aura of raw, masculine power emanated from him.

His lips curved faintly several times as if he found something in the acticle amusing.

"I hope you don't believe everything you read, Helen," Alexander said when he finished the article.

"The article sounds plausible to me."

"Then you think I'm chivalrous to the point of being foolish enough to provoke the wrath of the U.S.S.R. and thereby jeopardize my shipping interests . . . and all to help a lady in distress."

"I think you are the type of man who is willing to take enormous risks to get whatever or whoever you want."

"Indeed?" His teeth flashed and his bold dark eyes laughed at her. "In spite of your . . . shall we say, inexperience . . . in other areas . . . you are an excellent judge of character." Gold cuff links glimmered at his wrists as he swept a chair back from the table and sat down across from her.

"I hope you will permit me to join you?" he asked.

He was dangerously near, and she felt her senses responding to his virile maleness. "Mr. Marianatos, I don't mind if you sit down because I . . . I . . . I was just leaving," she stuttered.

She pushed her chair back from the table and would have risen when his hand closed firmly over hers. Her rebel pulse leaped at his touch. "I was hoping that by this morning you might feel differently about what happened," he said quietly.

"I can assure you I feel exactly as I did last night," she said, hoping she sounded more convincing to him than she did to herself.

"All I did was make a perfectly logical mistake," he said.

"That is the way you see it. However, I remember a man who refused to believe me when I told him the truth, a man who brutally held me down and would have forced me to . . ." She broke off, realizing with a start that her feelings for him had changed. Last night she'd thought him a criminal; she'd been terrified of him. Now every time she looked at him or thought of him, she felt strangely alive, strangely excited. She no longer feared him—at least not in the same way. But he was equally dangerous, perhaps even more dangerous to her now—because her feelings *had* changed. "Mr. Marianatos, I do not wish to be rude, but you are pushing me to it," she said desperately. She was aware of thickly lashed onyx eyes watching her closely, eyes which she could not meet, because if she met them, she would be too flustered to finish what she intended to say. "You are not the kind of man I wish to know. Now, please, let me go, or I will be forced to summon the maître d'."

As if in afterthought, he said, "Helen, last night you dropped this in the hall." He pulled her glittering scarf from his pocket and handed it to her.

"Thank you," she said in a tight, awkward voice as she started to rise.

Politely, he rose from his chair, as well, and helped her from hers. She was very aware of him—so tall, so masterful, towering over her. The scent of his after-shave—expensive and pleasant—drifted from his smooth, bronzed jawline to her nostrils. He gave her a long, searching look. "I'll call you in Athens," he said at last. "Perhaps by then you will see me in a different light."

"Please . . . don't."

She would have run from him, but he arrested her flight by stepping between their table and the next, and thus blocking her path.

Why couldn't he understand that she couldn't trust herself to see him again? He was exactly the sort of man she had determined long ago to avoid. He was a man who was so effortlessly appealing to women he could treat women callously and they would still flock to him.

She remembered her own experience with him last night—the punishing brand of his lips searing hers.

"I *will* call you," he said in a slow, determined manner. "And I *will* see you again."

"I don't think so."

"Then you should remember your own assessment of my character. I am a man who usually gets what he wants—because I'm willing to take the necessary risks. I intend to see you again—one way or the other."

She listened to his words with impotent fury. She knew his type too well. He didn't care who he hurt as long as he got his way. Her anger against him increased. There was no way she could leave until he allowed her to do so. Once again she was in his power.

Suddenly, there was an uproar at the entrance of the dining room, and Alexander and she turned to see what was going on. Natasha Chernitzky was making her entrance. . . .

Natasha was the most beautiful woman Helen had ever seen. Her skin was the color and texture of rich cream; her abundant raven hair was drawn back into a chignon at the nape of her neck. Ignoring the hubbub around her, as though it were no more than her due, the dancer surveyed the room disdainfully. When her emerald eyes found Alexander, possessively, they lit in recognition. If she saw Helen, she gave no indication. She was a star, a prima ballerina, and Helen was of no more importance than an insect that might buzz in an annoying manner. Still, as Natasha approached them, Helen fancied that her eyes narrowed slightly in her direction.

Natasha wore navy-blue silk—someone's original—brilliant in its design for its very simplicity. The soft material rippled over her breasts and hips as she moved toward them with her long strides and easy grace.

"Alexis . . ." Hers were artfully honeyed tones, thickly accented.

"Natasha . . ." Forgetting Helen for the moment, he moved toward his friend, and Helen, not as grateful as she would have thought she'd be for the chance to escape him, ran from the dining room.

Dutifully, the tour group assembled around the little Greek tour director as he stopped in front of the fashionably elegant cliffside restaurant where they would dine. The tour director was pointing out the sights of Athens that sprawled like thousands of miniature marble blocks in the smoke-haze beneath them.

One week had passed since Helen's fateful encounter with the handsome Greek entrepreneur in his Paris suite. Since that night, she had not been able to get him out of her mind. At the most inopportune moments she would remember his virile handsomeness, his dark, intent gaze, the strength of his arms as he'd held her, the feel of his lips passionately possessing hers, and she would burn with the memory of it.

Why did she keep thinking of him? Why couldn't she forget him? Did she really find him so attractive—in a purely physical way—that she couldn't forget him? Or was it simply because she'd found him and the whole episode in his suite so deeply shocking? She remembered again his punishing lips claiming hers, and a strange tingling like an electric current raced through her. Just the memory of him . . . She looked down at her hand and saw that it was trembling. No man, no one, nothing had ever affected her in such a way. Why? She thought suddenly of the restricted life she'd led in boarding schools and then in the conservatory, and she was filled with a sense of yearning. She remembered the long years of practice at the piano. She was twenty-two years old, and she hadn't yet lived.

He had not called! Strangely, with an eagerness she was almost ashamed of, she'd found herself asking the hotel clerk nearly every day if there'd been any calls for her while she was out—as if she actually wanted him to call her. . . .

The tour director was telling his entourage that the pollution in Athens was the worst in Europe and that it was severely damaging the ancient ruins of the Acropolis. His lecture turned from pollution to the restaurant where they were going to eat.

"This is one of Athens' best restaurants. It is even a favorite of Alexander Marianatos. . . ."

Helen felt his name as if it were a shock. This was the second time today that the tour director had mentioned Alexander Marianatos. Only earlier this day when she'd lunched with the tour group in one of the colorful *tavernas* specializing in seafood that ringed the picturesque yacht basin of Tourkolimano, the tour director had proudly pointed out a magnificent yacht as Alexander's.

"And now," the little Greek said, "we go in . . . for cocktails. Then we dine early—American style. You remember that Greeks . . . because of the siesta . . . rarely eat dinner before the hour of ten."

"Well, I'd starve for sure by then," said Mrs. Holt, one of the plumper tourists, who was first in the line heading into the restaurant.

Helen fingered her wristwatch. Gary still hadn't arrived. In fact, she'd scarcely seen him since they'd reached Greece. She'd gone on a short trip to Crete, and he'd remained in Athens.

She'd last seen him this morning, before she'd set out on a city tour which had included Hadrian's Arch, the Zappeion Gardens, the tomb of the unknown soldier, and Syntagma Square. Their own motorcoach had broken down again, and a new bus had been hired for the tour. Gary, preferring to remain behind with Poros to tinker with the temperamental motorcoach, had refused to go on the tour.

Gary! A tour of Europe couldn't hold a candle to a greasy engine in need of repair!

"Aren't you coming, Helen?" Carol Mortimer asked.

"I'll be in in a minute. I want to wait out here just a little bit longer—for Gary."

"Are you sure he's coming? You know he doesn't always show up."

"Although he skips the tours, you'll notice he's usually around for the meals. I don't know what could be keeping him."

Carol laughed and went inside, leaving Helen outside to wait for her brother alone.

At least half an hour passed as Helen waited. The day had been brilliant—the naked rock of Greece shining in its naked light. She was glad now of the growing dusk. Beneath her, Athens was bathed in a pale, almost transparent, light. The marble of the Acropolis glowed gold.

At last she resigned herself to the fact that Gary wasn't coming. She turned toward the restaurant and went inside. Her friends were on their second round of cocktails and feeling very jolly—a mood she did not share. As she was smoothing the pleats of her ice-blue skirt under her and sitting down, the plump tourist, Mrs. Holt, pleaded, "Miss Freeman, won't you please play something for us on that piano over there . . . the way you did that night in Vienna?"

"Thank you for asking me, but I'd rather not."

Mrs. Holt persisted. "The waiter told us that the musicians won't arrive until ten. Our party will be over by then, and you know this is our last night together. Tomorrow we will all be home in New York."

It was difficult for people to understand that just because she was an accomplished musician, she did not always wish to play on command—especially when vacationing. Carol Mortimer and the other tourists joined in, saying that the waiter had already assured them it would be all right with the management if she played.

Reluctantly, Helen agreed to play one song. She sat down at the piano on the nearby stage. The piano was copper-plated to fit in with the *taverna* decor. She chose a Greek melody she'd heard in a *taverna* in Crete and began to play. The piano badly needed tuning, but no one seemed to notice.

The group of Americans clapped enthusiastically. Several of them embraced Greek-style around the shoulders and stepped out onto the dance floor. The beat grew faster and faster; Helen's fingers rippled effortlessly over the keys with the technical skill of someone who'd spent years practicing her instrument. She was improvising because she'd never seen the written music to the song, and occasionally she struck a wrong note. But no one could tell the difference. The boistrous group was too caught up in the passion of the music and the showoff antics of the dancers. They were all having fun. Helen was glad she'd agreed to play for them.

The mood of gaiety was infectious. Guests from other dining rooms spilled into the piano bar where the Americans were clapping and dancing.

A tall, dark man, attired in a crisp white linen suit that was expertly tailored, strode through one of the doorways, and Helen, immediately aware of his presence, looked up. Across the room filled with music, smoke, people, and laughter, incredibly her eyes met those of Alexander Marianatos. Flustered, she looked down at her fingers racing nimbly over the keys. She struck several false notes but played on. When she looked up again, she saw that he was lounging carelessly against the bar ordering a drink.

The bar was crowded now, and beside the people swarming on all sides of him he looked tall and powerful. He alone did not move, but his eyes betrayed his inner excitement. His black gaze that was strangely urgent never left her face. How arrogantly self-assured he appeared, how ruthlessly dominating. He was a man who would always seek to command, a man determined to acquire whatever he wanted from life, and when he could not . . . She could not imagine a situation in which he would not command.

With a sense of foreboding, Helen remembered his last words to her: "I intend to see you again—one way or the other."

The next time she looked up from the piano, she saw that he was gone. She searched the room frantically, and then to her alarm, she found him. He was seated alone at a table that was but a few yards from the piano; and when her eyes found his, he smiled. His teeth flashed bright white against his dark complexion. He carelessly raked his eyes over her with frank, knowledgeable admiration. She looked away—wildly agitated —and missed a note. She thought she heard him chuckle low, as if he knew she was nervous because of him and found it amusing.

It was impossible for her to deny the intensity of her own excitement. His gaze that was too intimate sent her pulse fluttering and left her curiously without breath. Her fingers trembled on the keys.

If she hated him . . . why did she feel so . . . so alive whenever he was present? Without being able to stop herself, she remembered the fire of his touch. Her cheeks stung, and she hoped the dim light concealed her quick blush.

Helen finished the piece of music and stepped down from the piano. The room was strangely quiet; suddenly there was a burst of wild applause. She murmured something into the nearby microphone and searched the room wildly for some means of escape.

She realized at once that her hopes to evade Alexander were futile. He was rising languidly from his table and approaching her.

"Good evening, Helen." He smiled warmly; his eyes went over her slender body. She wondered if he thought her gauche and immature in her simple cotton dress with the modestly high neckline when he compared her to sophisticated women he knew, women like Natasha.

"Hello, Mr. Marianatos."

"Alexander," he corrected. "In spite of our brief acquaintance, don't you think we know each other rather too well to stand on such formalities?" he asked softly, smiling again as if he delighted in the swift color that came into her cheeks as she remembered they'd met one another in his bed.

"Mr. Marianatos, I'm dining here tonight with friends," she replied stiffly.

He caught her hand in his and drew her across the room out onto the terrace that overlooked Athens. The walls of the restaurant were whitewashed, and a rooftop garden had been planted.

"Why don't you let me take you to dinner tonight?" he asked. "I know this is a last-minute invitation, but I was unexpectedly detained in Paris for the past week. . . ."

Jealousy—unexpected and violent—winged through

her. Had he remained so long in Paris to be with Natasha?

"How did you find me—here?"

"Before your tour group left Paris, I obtained your itinerary from your tour director."

"You bribed him?" Rather than horrifying her as it should have, the thought delighted her.

"I can see that your poor opinion of me persists," he mocked. "No, I didn't bribe him."

"You shouldn't have troubled yourself to come here. I told you in Paris I never wanted to see you again."

"So you did, but I didn't believe you."

"Why not?"

"Because you are either a woman who does not yet know her own mind, or one who, knowing it, stubbornly refuses to give in to it."

He spoke of her as though she were a witless child, and she resented it.

"You know nothing about me!" she stormed.

"Nevertheless, what I know of you, I like." He paused, and she knew he was remembering the way he'd met her. His dark, intense gaze sent thrilling shivers racing down her spine. "I insist that you come to dinner with me," he continued. "This place is not Greece, although I will concede it has excellent food. Let a Greek who knows Athens show it to you."

His low-pitched voice had a seductive quality that confused her.

"Mr. Marianatos, I . . . I've told you . . . I never want to see you again. And I mean it. And that includes dinner . . . tonight."

He lifted her hand to his lips and, turning it over, kissed her wrist. The movement of his lips on her flesh tickled warmly. She gasped and tried to draw back, but he held her to him.

"What are you doing?" she cried out. "You mustn't!"

"I'm wondering if you dislike me as much as you pretend. Your pulse is pounding like a rabbit's." He released her, and she pulled her hand away. "Come to dinner with me tonight, Helen. I want to make up to you for the way I treated you when I found you . . . in my bed."

"Oh! You know I don't like you to refer to what happened so crudely!"

"I didn't realize I was being crude. I thought I was merely stating a fact."

"You seem to enjoy remembering it and reminding me of it."

"I find the memory of you—in bed with me—pleasant," he answered huskily.

"Well, I don't!"

"Don't you?" Again, the disturbingly husky tone in his voice. "As I said before, I think you are a woman who is afraid to admit what she feels." His gaze traveled slowly from her lushly sensuous lips, which were slightly parted, to her rounded curves, primly draped with ice-blue cotton pleats. For no reason at all she felt oddly warm. He smiled. "But for your sake, once again I will let the gallant part of my nature assert itself, and I promise you, I will not mention that night again—unless you bring it up. We can pretend that tonight we are meeting for the first time."

"I do not wish to play games."

"Neither do I."

"Mr. Marianatos, it is clear to me that you are used to getting your way in all things. Indeed, you are determined to do so! You take what you want! You don't care who you step on, who you hurt! You don't seem to understand the meaning of the word 'no.' "

In the darkness she could not see his face, but she sensed he was suddenly angry.

"And you, Miss Freeman, are beginning to make sense to me," he retorted abruptly. "I see why you've never had a boyfriend or a lover. You are as cold as the snow that caps Mount Olympus. If you persist in such behavior, you are likely to enjoy a very lonely old age. I doubt there are many men who would pursue you as I have."

With that, he turned from her and began stalking toward the entrance to the dining room.

His words struck deep. He was not the first man who'd accused her of coldness. But he was the first she'd ever cared about. As she watched his retreating form, she was miserable. She realized that strangely, impossibly, foolishly, she cared very much.

Her lips twisted into an ironic half-smile. She'd told herself that she would be different from her mother, that she would make herself immune to the appeal of this type of man. He was like her father—effortlessly appealing to women. Doubtless, Alexander treated the women in his life with the same careless ruthlessness her father had inflicted on her mother. A swift, painful vision of her mother flitted through Helen's mind. Her death had been a merciful release. Helen had been only sixteen at the time, when she had died after a lingering illness. Helen could still remember her father's callous indifference.

She knew *him;* at least she knew his *type* so well. But in spite of that fact, some rebel part of herself longed to go with Alexander and was ready to reject all the wisdom she'd acquired in such a terrible way. She yearned to spend . . . just one evening with him.

This was her last night in Greece. What could possibly happen in one evening?

Across the darkness her voice was a thin, fragile sound, stopping him. "Alexander . . ."

Chapter Three

Helen was glad of Alexander's strong brown fingers gripping her hand tightly as he led her through the hordes of tourists and Greeks that crowded the twisting, narrow streets of the Plaka, once the old city, now the "fun" place in nighttime Athens. The beat of bouzouki music throbbed; the twang of electronic guitars sounded from discothéques. She was breathless as the street they were following ended abruptly in a flight of steep, whitewashed steps. Alexander began mounting the steps, pulling her gently behind him. When she thought she couldn't walk another step, the stairs opened onto a rooftop *taverna* right under the long rocks of the Acropolis. Directly above them, she saw the ancient ruins of the Parthenon glowing in the moonlight.

"Oh, it's so beautiful," she gasped, her gaze wandering from the ruins to the picturesque *taverna*.

Strings of colored lights illuminated brightly painted tables scattered about on the roof. Geraniums growing in oil cans were splashes of red.

The headwaiter came, and, recognizing Alexander at once, began rapidly speaking Greek. He led them to a table beneath a vine-covered pergola that was private from the other diners.

Before dinner Alexander ordered retsina, a resinated white wine, for himself, and a glass of Pallini, a white wine, for Helen.

The wine came, and sipping hers slowly, she stared up at the ruins. After a while she grew aware that Alexander was studying her face as intently as she studied the Acropolis. She turned toward him with a start, suddenly feeling gauche and awkward—very much the tourist.

To cover her nervousness, she attempted conversation. "What is retsina?"

"It is wine with a touch of resin added to it," he said in low, melodious tones. "In former times the wine casks used to be lined with a resiny pitch, which not only caulked the seams, but helped preserve the wine. We Greeks grew to like the flavor imparted by the cask resin, and we now deliberately add it. I suppose there's a lesson there. Humans are a strange breed. If you accustom us to something—or someone—for a long enough period of time—even if that something . . . or someone . . . is not altogether pleasant—we grow to like the thing . . . or the person." He paused meaningfully.

"What are you trying to say?"

"That if you gave me half a chance, you might decide I'm not the monster you think I am."

She looked up at him. The fire in his eyes sent her pulse leaping, and she looked away, more flustered now than before.

Oh! She knew she shouldn't have come! He seemed so sincere! It was difficult—too difficult—for her to keep her guard up.

"I thought we were talking about wine," she said, hoping to divert him.

"I don't want to talk about wine; I want to talk about you."

"I'm really not a very interesting subject of conversation."

"Oh, but you are—to me."

She couldn't meet his virile gaze. "I-I wouldn't know where to start."

"We will start with what I already know, and you can fill in the gaps. You speak French, you are a gifted pianist, and you're touring Europe with your brother. You are a puzzling mixture of sophistication and . . . inexperience."

At his last word, she flushed. "I suppose in some ways I'm not your typical middle-class American girl," she conceded, unaware that her voice had filled with longing. "Although, in spite of being able to speak French and play the piano, I am quite average in all other respects."

"You are hardly average," he contradicted. "I have never met anyone like you before."

His words, coupled with the intensity with which he spoke them, filled her with a strange tension. Suddenly, she was as shyly tongue-tied as a teen-ager on her first date. Miserably, she twisted the fringes of her napkin.

"Tell me about this brother of yours," Alexander prompted gently, perhaps realizing that it would be easier for her to talk about someone other than herself.

"Gary—well . . ." She sighed heavily. "There's really not much to tell. I suppose he's like most sixteen-year-olds. His most notorious trait this summer, at least as far as our tour director is concerned, is that he is *always* late. That's a habit that becomes a nuisance when you're on a tour where every minute is accounted for."

She told him of the time in Madrid when baggage and tourists had been loaded onto the bus for departure to

Granada, only to be delayed two hours because of Gary.

"Where was he?"

"In Retiro Park consoling a child whose motorized airplane had crashed into a tree."

"I think I rather like your Gary."

"You see how it is," Helen said, warming to him because of his sympathetic answer. "He makes you wait for hours while he does some good deed it's impossible to fault him for."

"It sounds to me a tightly scheduled tour of Europe's cultural sights is the last thing a sixteen-year-old boy like Gary should be subjected to," Alexander said, startling her because she herself had thought the very thing before embarking on the tour with Gary.

"That's exactly what I tried to tell Hal."

"Who's Hal?"

"My father. I tried to convince him Gary would hate the tour, but he wouldn't listen. . . ." She broke off, remembering the only reason she and Gary had been sent on their European tour was to keep them abroad— out of her father's way—for the summer.

Hal had recently remarried and moved to New York City. He'd purchased a plush, but too small, Park Avenue town house. A visit from his grown children was an inconvenience he could affort to do without, she reminded herself bitterly.

"Helen, why do you call your father 'Hal'?"

Pain twisted her lips into a thin, tight line before she forced a smile that she hoped looked more natural than it felt. "He asked me to. I suppose it makes him feel younger . . . less . . . fatherly."

"And your mother?" Alexander asked, as if he sensed Hal was a painful subject.

"My mother is dead."

46

"I'm sorry." A glint of some emotion came and went in his dark eyes.

"It happened a long time ago," she said. "I hardly ever think of it anymore." That wasn't exactly true. The tragedy had deeply affected her; it still affected her.

She sipped her wine. The musicians began strumming a hauntingly romantic melody. Overhead, a sprinkle of stars dotted the night-black sky.

Alexander loomed closer. Before she could evade his large brown hand, his covered hers, his thumb sliding across the flesh of her wrist, rubbing the exact spot where her pulse quickened at his touch.

"Helen, would you like to dance?" he asked in resonant, well-modulated tones that were oddly pleasant to the ear.

He rose—a tower of virile masculinity. The black heat of his gaze melted all her coldness toward him.

He helped her from her seat and led her across the rooftop to a darkened dance floor.

She was feverishly aware of him as a man as he drew her into the hard circle of his arms. She caught the musky scent of his after-shave. A storm of sensations raced through her as he, holding her closely to him, led her through a series of dance steps with expert ease. Without realizing what she was doing, her hand that rested on the white linen collar of his suit drifted upward slightly to finger his thick black hair, which curled at the nape of his neck. He lowered his head to hers, and the warmth of his rough chin lightly brushed the smoothness of her forehead. Somehow—strangely —she felt so right in his arms. Their swaying bodies moved in perfect accord together.

The music stopped—much too soon—and slowly, as if he did so reluctantly, he released her.

For a long moment he gazed down at her, a slow, sensual smile curving his lips. His masculinity was disturbing, and her rebel pulse responded erratically, skipping beats.

"They've brought our dinner," he said softly.

"Have they?" Helen tried unsuccessfully to swallow the breathless catch in her own voice."

Dinner was as Alexander had promised—Greek. An appetizer of *dolmades*—little packets of flavored rice wrapped in vine leaves—preceded *moussaka*, a segment of luscious pie made of layered eggplant, minced lamb, cheese, tomatoes, eggs, and spices. It was so rich that Helen couldn't eat it all.

Alexander observed her thoughtfully. "Many tourists do not like Greek food." His alert gaze flicked to her unfinished plate.

"Oh, no. You mustn't think that. I'm glad you brought me here. This is the first opportunity I've had to eat a genuine Greek meal. The food was wonderful, but I'm quite full."

"And I'm glad you liked it. Few foreigners are neutral about Greek food," he commented with a wry smile that made the corners of his lips quirk in a most attractive way. "Some of our cooks are a little heavy-handed with the olive oil."

He continued speaking of Greek food, summing up by saying that one could hardly dismiss as culinary barbarians a nation that invented the chef's tall, puffy hat.

"And how did they come to invent it?" she asked, intrigued.

"It was derived from our Greek priests' black, flat-topped stovepipes when our famous cooks fled into the monasteries."

Conversation flowed naturally between them. Helen grew aware of her growing easiness in Alexander's company. He spoke of Greece, of Marianatos—the quaintly beautiful island in the Aegean his family owned—and of his yacht.

So deftly that she scarcely noticed that he did so, he maneuvered her into talking about herself. She found herself telling him how her father's career as an oil executive had forced her family to live all over the world, how she and Gary had thus been sent away to boarding schools, how in her loneliness she'd turned to music and had grown so accomplished she'd eventually chosen to make it her career.

Time seemed to pass quickly, and Helen realized with a start she'd never enjoyed being with anyone as much. She felt totally contented. The meal, the wine, and his ability to make her feel at ease had relaxed her. She'd let down her guard.

While he ordered American coffee for her and Greek-Turkish coffee for himself, she studied his handsome features. His thick raven hair fell roguishly across his brow; his black eyes flashed with vitality.

This same, powerful vitality was part of the charm that had magically overpowered her resistance to him and lulled her into feeling a false sense of security in his presence.

In spite of herself, she was discovering things about him she liked. She liked the courteous way he listened to her, letting her talk without interrupting her—as if he considered that what she had to say was important. She felt the musical quality—soft as velvet—of his low-pitched voice almost as though it were a caress. She liked the way his lips quirked when he was slightly amused by something she said.

But, most of all, she liked the way she felt because she was with him.

Just being with him gave the world a golden glow. She was dangerously attracted to him. It was as if something about him compelled her response. She studied the firm, yet sensual, shape of his mouth. Wantonly, her thoughts returned to the memory of his lips on hers, and she shivered, coloring just as he looked across the table at her, having finished his lengthy conversation with the waiter.

To cover her agitation, she looked quickly, but not quickly enough, away.

"What were you thinking of just then, Helen?" Alexander asked.

Momentarily shocked by the directness of his question, she was speechless with alarm. She couldn't possibly confess the truth.

"I . . . I . . . don't have any idea," she floundered, aware of a pulse beat thudding wildly in her throat.

"I hope you don't stare at every man with that wistfully vulnerable look on your face. It's enough to make me want to . . ." He severed the rest of that sentence abruptly, and stared moodily past her, clenching his fist.

Then deliberately he unclenched his hand and reached for his demitasse cup. The hard, masculine lines of his face were a mask of control.

The violence of his reaction alarmed her.

"Alexander, did I . . . is something wrong?"

His hand reached across the table and gripped hers. Again his black eyes studied her face, and, seeing that her distress was genuine, his grim expression softened. "No, it isn't you. . . . It's just that . . . sometimes . . . it's hard for me to believe you're for real. The way you were looking at me—I can't believe you don't know exactly what you're doing. With some women as beautiful as you, such glances are a practiced art," he finished.

And he had a great deal of experience with such

women, she reminded herself. Remembering the sophisticated beauty of Natasha Chernitzky, a jealous pang churned her stomach.

A practiced art. Was his own all-too-potent charm a masculine version of that art? Was he sincere at all, or just so effortlessly appealing he seemed so?

"Let's get out of here," he rasped harshly, interrupting her own unhappy thoughts. "After all, I have only a few hours to show you *my* city."

If she were wise, she would insist that he drive her at once to her hotel. But it was difficult to act wisely when she was in the company of a man whose magnetic presence acted on her like an elemental force, charging her with a strange excitement such as she'd never experienced before.

Helen's hair curled like smoke in the breeze gusting up the side of Mount Lycabettus. She was keenly aware of Alexander's fingers lightly touching the back of her waist as he escorted her out onto the flagstone terrace of the elegantly expensive restaurant atop the nine-hundred-foot hill overlooking *his* city. Other couples sitting at small tables in red upholstered chairs relaxed over drinks.

Alexander had ordered the Greek liqueur, ouzo, for them to sip while they enjoyed the panorama of a sparkling Athens spread beneath them.

"Oh, Alexander, the view is breathtaking."

"It's even better at sundown, when you can catch Athens going from white to gold."

Beneath them amidst the shimmering white lights, the streets flowed like inky ribbons. He picked out the sprinkle of red, blue, and green neon that were Syntagma and Omonia squares. Farther to the left, the white and green beacon of the airport flashed. Behind

Syntagma she saw the Acropolis, its temples glowing like a jeweled crown, and around its base the tightly packed twinkling of the Plaka.

"My shipping offices are over there," he said, pointing beyond to the seaport, Piraeus. I have offices downtown, as well."

Dimly, she could make out off-lying ships that were lit from bow to stern.

They lapsed into silence. Alexander's mood had been dark ever since they'd left the Plaka. She realized suddenly that since they'd left the restaurant where they'd eaten dinner, she'd done almost all the talking. Indeed, she'd chattered the whole time they'd ridden the funicular up the side of Mount Lycabettus. He'd spoken only when she'd asked him a direct question about some landmark.

He was the first to break the lengthening silence.

"Helen, do you think you'd enjoy the walk down to the car more than riding the funicular."

"A walk would be nice. . . ."

Had she realized the pathway down Mount Lycabettus was famed as Athens' lovers' lane, she might not have agreed so readily.

Couples, tightly embraced, were nestled in secluded niches beneath thickly dark evergreens. Although Alexander walked silently beside her without touching her, every nerve fiber in her body was keenly aware of him.

Above, a lopsided moon hung in the night-black sky. The stars shone clearly, only slightly touched by the smoke and haze of the city.

This was her last night to be in Athens, to be with *him*. She sighed achingly, wondering what he was thinking.

Suddenly the pathway plunged unexpectedly, and

she would have fallen had Alexander not quickly grabbed her. One of his large tanned hands wrapped around her waist, the other clutching her elbow, steadying her. His touch was jolting, like an electric charge rocketing through her. She gasped. Becoming instinctively aware because of his own swift intake of breath that he was no more impervious to her nearness than she was to his, she felt strangely joyous.

He was staring down at her—his dark gaze hypnotically compelling—dragging her with him into the undercurrents of his desire.

The fire in his eyes kindled an answering flame in her. Excitement like a conflagration out of control quivered through her nervous system.

If only he would release her, perhaps sanity would return.

But he did not release her. It seemed to her some man-woman force—basic and elemental—a power outside themselves, stronger than both of them, drove them. She could only stare deeply into his eyes while his hands slowly ran the length of her naked arms. His fingers locked tightly with hers, and he pulled her body to his. Unresisting, she allowed him to mold her soft curves to his hard length. She shivered first with cold and then from the warmth of his touch as the fire of desire licked through her veins.

As his dark head bent toward hers, she stretched onto her tiptoes to shorten the distance that separated their lips. He crushed her to him with a groan, his firm mouth exploring the corner of her lips before claiming them fully.

She was innocent and responded to him out of blind instinct. Her fingers relaxed in the grip of his, and she drew them away without even knowing that she did so to move them beneath his coat and caress the solid warmth of his back beneath the crisp material of his shirt.

His kiss wiped her mind blank. There was only a wild thrilling darkness enveloping her. Only strong arms holding her tightly, only hot, moist lips possessing hers with a skillful and ruthless completeness.

Somehow, her arms wound around his neck, her fingers curling into the ebony blackness of his hair. Her lips trembled beneath his.

Slowly, Alexander lifted his head from hers and looked down at her, seeing too clearly in the silvery moonlight the soft surrender in her beautiful face. Her blue eyes still shone with desire. Her lips, swollen from his masterful kisses, were parted in a dazed half-smile. He drew in a deep breath, curbing his passion.

To Helen, the world seemed to spin beneath her feet. She was glad of Alexander's steadying grip at her elbow. It was some time before she grew aware of his hard scrutiny.

He looked grim, forbidding. Remorse at her wanton behavior washed over her. What must he be thinking of her? Why had she responded to him so shamelessly?

It was shattering to discover that this man, the very type of man she'd always been so careful to avoid, could make her lose control simply by kissing her. His appeal, which was effortless on his part, was terrifying to her.

Oh, why had she gone out with him? Why had she been so foolhardy?

Even now as she studied his grimly handsome features, she longed for him, for his possessive embrace. All the feelings she'd so carefully suppressed by burying herself in her muscial career were erupting inside her like a volcanic force.

She was desperately drawn to a man who would

destroy her if she gave him the chance and not even care that he did so.

But she was not going to give him that chance!

Even as his hands sought hers to pull her to him once more, she jerked free of his embrace, holding her own body stiffly apart from his.

"It's late," she said shakily. "And I think I should be getting back to the hotel—to pack."

"Are you more afraid of me, or yourself, little one?"

"I-I'm not . . . afraid," she lied, realizing the husky tremor in her voice probably betrayed her true feelings.

"Then what is wrong? A minute ago, you . . ."

A minute ago she'd practically melted in his arms, behaving with baffling shamelessness—and with a man who was hardly more than a stranger! She flushed hotly at his words.

"I-I don't know why th-that happened. But I realize . . . now . . . that it was a mistake."

"Why? If two people enjoy one another's company, why shouldn't they kiss each other? We're adults—not children."

The deep tones of his voice seemed to vibrate through every nerve end in her body. Did he have any idea what just the sound of his voice could do to her? She felt a desperate need to end this conversation.

"You're a very warm and beautiful woman, and I want you," he continued huskily. Again his voice filled her with a strange longing. He took a step toward her, and she backed away.

"D-don't come near me," she choked hoarsely, wondering how her words could sound so harsh when she felt herself melting inside. "I don't want you to touch me again!"

"You don't really feel that way."

She had to say something to convince him before her

treacherous feelings swamped her. "I do! And I'm glad I'll be leaving tomorrow, because if I weren't you might bully me into seeing you again."

"Is that what you think I did tonight?"

Her voice barely wavered as she remembered fleetingly how intensely she'd longed to spend just one evening with him.

"Well . . . yes . . ."

"Liar. I'd given up on you, and you called me back. And now that I've had an evening with you, I find that it isn't nearly enough. I want you to postpone your departure."

"Postpone my departure?"

"Why not? It would give us a chance to see if this attraction between us is based on anything more substantial than physical desire."

Was her presence as uniquely unsettling to him as his was to her? At the thought, a delicious shiver shuddered through her.

He moved toward her, and when she backed away, he caught her by the wrist.

"Better watch where you're going," he murmured. "Remember, you're standing on the edge of a mountain." He caught her to him and held her tightly, as though she were very precious to him. She heard the rapid thudding of his heart, felt her soft curves pressed against the lean contours of his body.

She drew in a shaky breath as she glanced over the edge of the rocky precipice.

It was the height, she told herself frantically—not him!—that made her feel so breathless and dizzy.

"I was in no danger of falling," she said, trying to wrench herself free.

"I'm beginning to think lying is a defect in your

character," he taunted softly. "We must work on that together."

"We are not going to work on anything together!" she stormed. She placed her hands on his chest and pushed with all her might, but he held her with an effortless ease that maddened her. "You are going to take me home—now."

"No, I'm not. Now—I'm going to kiss you again." He was bending his face to hers, staring deeply into her eyes for a long moment. "You want me to as much as I want to. Admit it."

"I don't!"

"Then why are you limp and quivering in my arms?"

She would have denied that, too, had his lips not covered hers. Then his fierce passion crushed all resistance from her. Involuntarily, the hands that had been futilely pressing against his chest moved downward and slipped around his waist.

No other experience in her life—not even her music—had ever aroused her like this. She wanted him so much that in that moment she had no regard for the consequences.

When he moved his lips from hers, all she could feel was regret that he had done so.

"Will you postpone your departure tomorrow," he muttered thickly, "and stay in Greece with me?" He pressed a gentle kiss upon each closed eyelid. When she did not answer, he said, "If you're worried about money, I'd pay all your additional expenses."

The mention of money was like a splash of ice water on fire. Her passion cooled.

Obviously he thought so little of her he was asking her to be his mistress!

She summoned the shreds of her control and began in a ragged whisper, "Alexander, I've told you my feelings. I have no intention of remaining in Greece. Not for an extra day! Not even an hour! I don't particularly like you or your forceful tactics, and I'll be glad to put tonight and you behind me for good!" She ignored the hollow pain in the pit of her stomach that the thought of never seeing him again had produced.

A muscle flexed near Alexander's jawline.

"All right," he said smoothly, releasing her. His expression was an unemotional mask. "In spite of your accusations, I have no intention of forcing you to do otherwise."

She was surprised. Somehow, she'd expected a different reaction, and she felt vaguely disappointed. Apparently, whether he acquired her as his new mistress or not was of little importance to him. Doubtless, any pretty girl would do—for a man like him.

She chided herself for being so ridiculous. She should be feeling relief. She was beginning to realize that if he desired her company, there would be little she could do to prevent him from enjoying it. Somehow, he had the ability to control her as no other man had.

They walked down the mountain without talking to the pearl-gray Rolls, where Alexander's chauffeur quickly squashed out his cigarette in the dust of the street and respectfully rushed to open Helen's door for her.

When she was snugly tucked into the back seat of the car, Alexander got in beside her. He lifted his arm and placed it on the back of the seat so that if Helen was not very careful, the back of her head brushed against it. Although it was her firm desire to avoid any physical contact with the man, she could not prevent the treacherous thought that being wrapped in his arms in the back seat of his car would be a very pleasant sensation.

What was happening to her? Five minutes ago he'd asked her to be his mistress, and she still wanted him as much as ever.

The big engine purred, and the Rolls sped almost silently through the streets of the elite Kolanaki district beneath the southeast slope of Lycabettus. Absently, Helen noted the fabulous residences stacked against the hillsides.

For a while they sat silently. Then Alexander began an impersonal discussion, pointing out some of the sights, as if nothing out of the ordinary had happened between them. She thought he did so to pass the time. In spite of herself, she became absorbed in the conversation.

He pointed to a modern, soaring glass building that slashed the inky skyline. "My office in Athens is up there—in the penthouse. If you were staying longer, I would have you visit me tomorrow. The view is excellent."

She remembered the fabulous view of Paris from his hotel suite.

"I'm beginning to think you like heights," she said.

"I do. Just as much as you are afraid of them."

"How did you know that?" she asked, a little shocked at the accuracy of his statement.

"Observation. Just as I know heights are not the only thing you're afraid of. . . ."

A slow blush warmed her skin as she detected the faintly suggestive quality in his voice.

Uneasily, she realized that very little escaped his attention. She would be wise not to underestimate his abilities in the future. The future . . . That was something the two of them would not have. . . . Again this realization upset her, and she fingered the handles of her purse nervously.

The chauffeur swerved unexpectedly, and Helen was thrown closely against Alexander. Automatically, he moved his arm that was resting on the back of the seat downward, circling her slim body in a protective fashion as he held her against his own hard warmth.

Then leaning forward, he and his driver exchanged rapid Greek.

The tension drained from his body as he sank back next to her.

"Nothing to be alarmed about," Alexander reassured her in English.

She noticed that he did not remove his arm from her shoulders.

"So tomorrow you're leaving Greece," he began.

A quiver of apprehension raced down her spine. She'd thought that had been definitely settled.

"Yes . . ."

She was relieved when he merely asked, "And did your tour of our country include a visit to the National Archaeological Museum?"

"I spent one morning there."

"One morning . . . A week would be inadequate to see everything."

"It was one of the most fascinating museums I've ever seen."

"It is internationally incomparable," he said in that supremely confident manner that was characteristic of him.

He began speaking of Greek art and antiquities. It was easy to see that he was an expert in the field. Vaguely, Helen did think it was taking them a very long time to reach her hotel, but she became so fascinated by his explanation of the Mycenaean culture that the thought was pushed to the back of her mind.

"I just got a glimpse of the Mycenaean exhibits," she exclaimed. "I kept telling myself I'd make time for another visit to the museum, but there was always something else to do."

"Now be honest. I think most tourists find museums dull. Would you . . . really . . . have liked to see more antiquities?"

"Oh, yes!"

She thought she heard him murmur, "I think that could very easily be arranged."

"But I'm leaving tomorrow, and the museum closed hours ago."

He was not listening to her. He was speaking Greek again in a commanding fashion to his chauffeur.

The big car made a quick right and then another. Was she only imagining that they were retracing the route they'd previously driven?

She peered out the window as buildings and street corners whisked by. It was impossible to be sure.

Suddenly, the car was twisting up an incline and braking; the chauffeur's automatic window lowered silently and he spoke into a security-system microphone. A wrought-iron gate opened. Then once more the car was climbing.

Helen sprang out of Alexander's arms and looked out the rearview mirror just as the electrically powered gate swung shut behind them.

Ahead of them she saw a brilliantly lit, multi-storied white palace perched high upon its hill like a Byzantine monastery. Once more the Rolls braked, this time in front of towering marble columns—a grand entranceway.

She turned wildly to confront Alexander. His lean, hard face was expressionless.

"Where have you brought me?" she accused.

"To my home," he responded in even tones, as if there was absolutely nothing wrong with that fact.

"But why?"

Even as she blurted out the question, she knew it was unnecessary. He had brought her here for one reason only—to seduce her.

He lifted a finger to smooth the crease between her worried brows. The grooves beside his mouth deepened, and he smiled. In spite of her misgivings about him, Helen warmed toward him.

"I can almost read that racing mind of yours, Helen," he teased softly. You think I've brought you here to seduce you, don't you?"

She squirmed uncomfortably, feeling on the defensive. Yet he was the one who was behaving abominably —taking advantage of her!

"W-Well, did you?"

To her horror, he made no denial. "Why don't you come inside and see?" he mocked.

Alexander's warm brown hand gripped Helen's as he effortlessly pulled her from the car.

"You had no right . . ." she sputtered. "No right at all . . . to bring me here."

"I did so only because I thought you would enjoy it," he answered innocently.

"What could I have possibly said or done to make you think that of me?" She stopped in horror, biting her tongue at the disgraceful memory of herself in his arms, clinging to him every time he kissed her. She reddened.

A brief flash of white teeth against brown skin; black eyes raked her as he read her mind. She knew that he found the memory of their embrace, as well as her present discomfiture, pleasurable. Doubtless he thought he could very easily seduce her—and remembering her own response to him, she couldn't be entirely certain of her own ability to resist him.

She was definitely in over her head. How in the world was she going to get out of this one?

Chapter Four

"I'm not going inside," Helen said firmly as Alexander propelled her up a gracefully swirling flight of marble steps laced with delicate stone railings. He paused before enormous, polished double doors.

At the touch of his key in the lock, the doors swung open.

"I said I'm not . . ."

"Of course you're coming in," he contradicted.

But when slender fingers curved over the edges of the stone balustrade in a death grip, he did not physically force her.

Instead, he said, "Or do you feel safer . . . outside . . . in the dark . . . alone . . . with me?"

Again she caught a faintly mocking note in his deep voice. His black eyes gleamed as if he were amused.

Glancing back over her shoulder, she saw that the chauffeur had disappeared. The Rolls, still parked in the drive, mirrored night lights.

Nerveless, her fingers loosened. Surely inside such a grand house there would be servants. Perhaps she could persuade one of them to help her. Numbly, she allowed herself to be led into an elegantly appointed foyer.

She scarcely noticed the fragrance of freshly cut flowers enveloping her. She was conscious only of the hushed stillness of the house stretching endlessly on all sides of her. She stood frozen—inches from the door.

Where were his servants? Asleep?

"We are quite alone," he said, as if in answer to her unspoken question. "I gave my servants the day off."

Nervousness moistened her palms with perspiration as she clasped and unclasped them. The only sounds in the house were those of the mad pumping of her own pulse beats against her eardrums and the stiff crinkling of paper as, idly, he sifted through a pile of neatly sorted mail on a black, lacquered table beneath a cut-crystal chandelier.

His lavish home, his elegant white linen attire, and his own suave demeanor did not conceal the latent power of his muscular body. *And she was alone with him!*

Never had she felt more vulnerable.

"All of them—gone?" She faltered.

At the unnatural sound of her voice, he turned and smiled a smile that devastated her senses.

"Yes. Except for the guards outside and Georgios, the chauffeur, we are alone."

Guards—but they were outside. There was no one to help her but herself!

He continued politely in the manner of a gracious host determined to set a nervous guest at ease. "Would you like a drink?"

Oh, the man, for all his polish, was a monster! She must remember that when she found herself slipping under the spell of his charm. Hadn't he brought her to his home in the dead of the night without her consent?

Hadn't he ever so conveniently given his servants the night off?

Under the circumstances a drink was the last thing she needed. "No," she replied in a voice she hoped sounded less nervous than she felt, "I don't believe I'll have anything."

"Hope you don't mind if I do. It's been a long day. I only got in from Paris late this afternoon. . . ."

Late this afternoon . . . Then he must have come directly from the airport to the restaurant to find her. Had he been that anxious to see her? For the first time she noticed the skin beneath his eyes was faintly shadowed.

He led her through several vast rooms—all different, yet blending harmoniously one into the other. They were airy, with high ceilings, tall windows, and elaborate furnishings. All of them contained flowers and an abundance of greenery which made the mansion, for all its formal grandeur, seem warmly alive.

His house, more like a splendid palace than a house, was a reflection of the man he appeared to be—grand, tasteful, and overpowering.

But it was not the house which electrified her senses; it was the man.

He showed her into a room that was smaller than the ones they had passed through. When he pressed the light switch on the richly panneled wall, she saw they were in his library.

Floor-to-ceiling bookshelves in dark-grained, gleaming wood spanned two walls. Against another wall was a fireplace above which hung a bold, modern painting. A series of glass doors opened onto a balcony that overlooked tennis courts and an enormous pool, glimmering like a blue jewel against the darkened grounds beyond.

A couch was upholstered in burgundy velvet; the rest of the colors were earth tones. The room was both masculine and warm.

Alexander stood at the bar. "Sure you won't have something—a Coke? Straight from the bottle." He opened one. "Laced with nothing stronger than a few ice cubes?" Ice tinkled invitingly into two crystal glasses. He poured the Coke into one, offering it to her. His lips parted in a disarming grin.

In spite of herself, she returned his smile with a tremulous one of her own.

"There, that's better. You don't look so tense now."

He handed her the drink, his fingers touching hers for the briefest instant.

"Helen, when will you realize you have nothing to fear from me?"

His black gaze was intense. She was aware of her own breathing—rapid and uneven. "The moment you deliver me safely to my hotel."

"You are safe right now." His voice was low—intimate.

"Safe . . . with . . . you . . . alone here?" He was so tall, so ruggedly *male*. Her knees felt rubbery at the thought of being alone with him, and she leaned against the sofa for support.

"Yes."

"You brought me here against my will."

He leaned back against the bar a safe distance from her with a languid ease that showed her clearly her accusation didn't ruffle him in the least. Black head tilted, he sipped his drink.

"That's not exactly true," he answered. "I knew if I asked you, your maidenly sense of proprieties would dictate a proper 'no.' "

"So you took matters into your own hands. . . ."

"It was you who gave me the idea," he returned smoothly.

"Me!" she blurted out, allowing anger to mask her true cause of anxiety. "How in the world did I . . ."

"You said you would enjoy seeing more antiquities. You seemed genuinely interested in them when we were talking in the car," he replied guilelessly, baffling her by his abrupt change of subject.

"I was, but what have antiquities got to do with anything?"

"Everything. I have one of the finest private collections in the world."

"Oh . . ."

"I thought you would enjoy coming here—to see my collection."

"I would. . . ." Her anger toward him dissolved.

Black eyes flashed with triumph. "Then . . . you admit that I was right, and you're glad I brought you to my home?"

"Not when you used trickery to do so," she said, stubbornly trying to cling to an emotion she no longer felt.

"I never tricked you."

"You told me you were taking me to my hotel."

Carelessly, he brushed back the thick lock of ebony hair that had fallen rakishly across his tanned brow. He eyed her steadily, making no apology for his behavior. "I was," he began patiently, "but when you were so enthusiastic about the Mycenaean exhibit, I changed my mind."

"You have an answer for everything," she murmured.

"When you know me better, you will find that I'm very direct. I go after what I want, without resorting to trickery."

Helen felt shaken by the determination in his admission, the ruthlessness she knew lay beneath it. When he wanted something, he allowed nothing to stand in his way.

"I have no intention of getting to know you better," Helen managed tautly. "You forget that tomorrow I'm leaving."

For an instant, anger blazed in the depths of his black eyes. He drew a deep, slow breath as he curbed it. Tossing his head back, he lifted the crystal glass to his chiseled mouth and drained its contents quickly.

"How can I forget when you find it necessary to keep reminding me of that fact?" he said. The passionate note in his voice vibrated through her.

"If I repeat myself, it's only because you don't seem convinced," she persisted stiffly.

"Perhaps I'm not."

"What?"

"Remember, I have the rest of tonight to persuade you to stay." His voice had gone low, melodious—thrilling.

She should have known she couldn't trust him!—"You never intended to show me your collection of antiquities," she accused in quavering tones as he spanned the distance that separated them in long, easy strides.

She shrank against the couch.

"Oh, but you're wrong. I'm going to show it to you now."

Now that he was so dangerously near her, she didn't dare raise her head to risk looking up at him for fear he would see how just his nearness aroused her. A tremor of some emotion she didn't fully understand throbbed through her. If he kissed her now she was lost . . . surely. . . .

When he brought his hand to her waist to escort her

to the salon which housed his collection, she jerked away, her heart racing in panic.

He did not attempt to touch her again. "This way," he said, pushing the door open for her and waiting for her to step through it.

Her high-heeled sandals clicked across glossy parquet floors as she hurried to keep up with him. He dialed the combination that turned off the alarm system that protected the collection. Then he led her through a pair of thick steel doors.

His collection—consisting of bronze and marble statuary, pottery, and wall hangings—was organized chronologically. He began a thorough, as well as fascinating, explanation of each piece. What interested her most were the anecdotes he told about his personal experiences at the archaeological sites when specific antiquities had been discovered.

An hour passed pleasantly without either of them noticing that it did so.

"But surely I'm boring you," he said at last, setting a piece of pottery down that had once belonged to the great, ancient sculptor, Phidias.

"Oh, no!" she protested. "You've made it all come to life!" She couldn't suppress the enthusiasm that filled her voice. "I had no idea such patience and skill went into retrieving these pieces."

"As well as hard work and money."

He reset the alarm and led her from the room.

She was about to mention the time and request that they return to her hotel, but before she could do so, he said, "I want to show you my favorite part of the house—the loft. It overlooks the pool, the gardens, and Athens."

They were retracing their steps down the long corridor.

"It sounds like another one of your high places," she said, laughing gently. She had forgotten for the moment to fear him.

"It is. I bought this house because of it. The previous owner was a Greek prince who was married to an Italian actress. He extensively remodeled the house to suit her whims. Beneath the loft is a theater—large enough to stage a genuine theatrical production."

"Do you ever use it?"

"Sometimes . . . I loan it to a friend who likes to rehearse here," he said evasively.

They had come to the end of the corridor. Alexander pushed open brass doors and paused for a moment, running his hand over a wall to locate the light switch. Then suddenly the theater was ablaze in all its golden and white glory. The seats were red velvet, the carpet scarlet plush. The walls were white with scrolls of gold.

"Why . . . it's beautiful," she murmured, awestruck.

"A little lavish," Alexander conceded. "Marie Antoinette would have approved of our Italian actress's tastes."

Helen ran lightly down the aisle to the stage. "Do you mind," she asked whimsically, "if I climb up to the stage?"

"Go right ahead." His mouth quirked and she knew her enthusiasm amused him.

As she moved eagerly about the stage, she noticed a ripple of pink satin peeping from beneath the heavy folds of the stage curtain. Reaching for it, she discovered it was attached to a worn ballet slipper that had been carelessly discarded.

"Sometimes . . . I loan it to a friend who likes to rehearse here," he had said.

Natasha!

The satin ribbons slipped painfully through her fingers, as though the smooth fabric burned. She was aware of a swift tightening in the pit of her stomach at the thought of Natasha . . . here . . . with him.

It was ridiculous of her to care about his being with another woman. But she did. All the bright gaiety that had possessed her seconds before was gone.

Helen's eyes traveled upward. Above the stage, rich, white, oak paneling vaulted. She could see white and gilt beams spanning the ornate ceiling.

"The loft is up there," Alexander said, pointing upward, unaware of her change in mood. "Come, we'll use the elevator. This is the only part of the house with so much wooden construction," he was saying as he inserted his key into the elevator. "Another whim of our actress. She thought stone—even marble—was cold."

Soon—because of Alexander's overwhelming magnetism—both the slipper and the dancer were forgotten. Helen and he were both laughing over another story about the actress as they stepped out of the elevator into a sitting room as luxuriously decorated as the theater.

Her feet sank into thick Persian carpet that stretched across a dark, glossy parquet floor. Draperies of the sheerest silk curtained sheets of glass spanning one side of the room. The large portrait of a beautiful girl heavily framed in gold hung over the marble fireplace. The bold slope to the high ceiling added architectural charm.

Helen found it difficult to believe anyone could be so wealthy.

The room, for all its grandeur, was comfortable. The furnishings were modern—chrome and glass; the dominating colors—blues, browns, and tans.

"I can't believe," Helen began, "that you refer . . . to all this . . . as 'the loft.' "

"Still another whim of our actress," he said, smiling.

He pressed a button and soft music filled the room.

"Come out onto the balcony," he said. Sheer draperies parted, flowing gracefully as he opened French doors that led out onto a stone terrace.

He grasped her hand so firmly in his that she could not withdraw it and drew her to the narrow balustrade.

Four stories beneath, a dark rectangular jewel of a pool sparkled. Catching her breath, Helen clung to Alexander. She had never been able to look over the edge of anything without feeling dizzy.

Scaling the side of the building like the frailest thread of a spider's web was a polished brass ladder.

"What's that for?" Helen asked breathlessly, pointing to the ladder.

"My version of a fire escape," Alexander returned in a curiously hard voice. "I told you before the loft is basically of wooden construction. I live up here. Once —long ago—I had a brush with fire and death." Abruptly, he changed the subject. "The terrace you're standing on belongs to the original house. Only the interior—the loft—was added by our actress." He paused and stared moodily out upon a twinkling Athens. After a long moment of silence, he said, "I think I'll have another drink. Would you like more Coke?"

"I'm fine. . . ." She would have to be leaving, in any case—as soon as he finished his drink.

She followed him inside. While he poured himself another drink, she walked around the loft noting the flowers, plants, and art treasures scattered about the room. As she fingered priceless knickknacks, she realized this room could have been a museum.

She had glided to the far end of the room and

through gold-trimmed doors before she realized she'd wandered into an enormous bedroom, mirrored dressing room, and bath.

She saw the vast bed covered in gold satin. Across it blazed a bird of fire. Her stomach somersaulted as suddenly the night she'd first met Alexander came back to her.

Again she'd stumbled by mistake into *his bedroom*. He'd said he lived up here. She hadn't really given that remark much thought. Now it took on a new meaning.

Almost immediately, unpleasant suspicions began forming in her mind. He'd brought her up to his bedroom! He'd said earlier he had the whole night to persuade her to stay in Greece! At the thought, her blood ran cold.

"And do you like my home, little one?" Alexander asked from right behind her in his deep, disturbingly husky voice.

She whirled to face him. In one hand he held a drink. To her dismay she observed his free hand deftly loosening the knot of his tie and unbuttoning the top two buttons of his shirt, revealing an unsettling amount of his bronzed, muscular chest. She saw the ragged scar that ran down his throat, as well as the glimmer of the same gold medallion she'd seen before.

Carelessly, he tossed the tie over a convenient, nearby chair before removing his coat and placing it on the same chair. He rolled up the cuffs of his long-sleeved shirt. No longer so formally attired, he seemed even more overpoweringly masculine.

Fear—unchecked—caused her heart to pound like a wild drumbeat as she clutched her throat. She was about to demand that he take her home at once when he began speaking, moving farther into his bedroom.

Because he was no longer so near and because he

began speaking about what seemed a "safe" topic of conversation, her fear of him lessened, although her pulse still throbbed unevenly.

"You may have wondered about the design on my bedspread," he said. "You probably remember it from Paris. . . ."

"Yes . . ." she replied uncertainly.

"A while ago I mentioned I'd had a brush with fire and death. . . ." He paused to sip his drink. "When I was a boy of twelve, my family lived in a tenth-story, twelve-room apartment here in Athens. One night when my parents were out, I woke up. I could hardly breathe. Smoke and flames were everywhere. Somehow I got to my baby sister Andrea's room and pulled her from her crib. There was no way out of the apartment except to jump from our balcony—either ten stories down or four feet across . . . to the balcony of another building.

"What did you do?"

"I jumped, with my sister in my arms, to the other building. A man who was standing there caught me."

"Oh, Alexander! What if he hadn't . . ."

"He almost didn't. You may have noticed a scar. . . ." Brown fingers traced the wicked line on his neck. "I cut myself that night—I don't even remember in what way. We never knew how the fire started. Nearly sixty people died, including the servants. But I was an instant hero. The newspapers labeled me a 'bird of fire.' The name stuck. I was even awarded an official medal." He pulled the medallion from beneath his shirt. "I wear it always—as a reminder that I can do *anything* if I'm determined enough."

"Where is Andrea now?"

"She lives with my family on Marianatos. The portrait above the fireplace is of her."

"She is very beautiful."

"I hope that someday soon you two will meet," he said, turning and moving toward her. His words, the casual inference she would be remaining in Greece to meet his sister, as well as his lazy approach, triggered an alarm in her.

"It's time for me to be going," she said shakily.

"Or maybe the time has come for me to persuade you to stay—indefinitely."

Blue eyes darted fearfully and met his own dark and very luminous ones for the briefest instant.

He reached for her to pull her into his arms.

"N-no. D-don't touch me!"

His hands fell to his sides. "All right," he replied reasonably. "Why don't we go in the other room and sit down? I think you would feel more at ease . . . with me . . . in there."

She slid past him into the sitting room. She did feel safer away from his bedroom, but she knew that this sense of safety was an illusion. She was trapped. The only way down was that precarious ladder or the elevator, to which only Alexander had a key. Remembering the sheer, four-story drop and her own terror of heights, she knew the ladder was definitely out. Somehow she had to get the key from him. She remembered him putting it in the pocket of his coat—the coat that was now in his bedroom.

"Why don't you sit down?" he said, indicating the blue couch across from the chair he himself sat on. When she hesitated, he added, "You'd be more comfortable."

Her knees seemed to give way, and she sank down onto the couch.

"Why are you so determined to leave tomorrow?" he asked.

Naturally, there were many reasons—but the foremost on her mind at the moment was to escape him and the tumultuous feelings he aroused in her.

"Well, for one thing . . . my job," she evaded. "In three weeks I'm to start as a music teacher in a girls' school in Connecticut."

"Three weeks is ample time to give notice," he said, casually dismissing her career as if it were of no more importance than breaking an engagement for the evening. "You can call them tomorrow—first thing—to tell them to hire a new teacher."

His arrogant attitude annoyed her, but she was determined to remain calm. "I couldn't do that. Bill is counting on me."

"Now we're getting to your real reason—Bill." His low, accusing voice—harsh, yet controlled—cut to her heart.

"It's not what you're implying," she retorted, a trace of anger edging her own voice.

The hard line of his lips twisted cynically. "Then what makes Bill so special?"

Alexander never moved his black eyes from her. He stood statue-still, the hard planes of his face seemed carved in granite.

Did he have any idea how much his looking at her like that intimidated her?

"H-he taught me . . . H-he was a former instructor of mine at the conservatory. He gave me more musically than anyone else, and when he was hired as the head of the music department in Connecticut . . . and one of his music teachers married unexpectedly . . ." She broke off. "I believe that I owe him more than I can ever repay."

"And working for him is the only payment your noble Bill expects for this debt of gratitude you feel so keenly. . . . Your being young and beautiful had nothing to do with his hiring you. . . ."

The contempt lacing his voice infuriated her. And to smear Bill—dear, sweet, harmless Bill. . . .

"If you want to know," she began, fury tinging her cheeks with warmth and causing her words to tumble out of her lips like bursts of gunfire, "I want to leave Greece tomorrow because I never want to see you again. I told you that in Paris, but you refused to believe me. Tonight I went out with you because I thought I might have been mistaken to judge you on the basis of what happened in your hotel room. But now you've thoroughly convinced me that you are a person ruled only by the basest of instincts."

"Is that so? And you are not?" There was a taunting quality in his rough voice that unnerved her.

Honesty forced her to admit, "At least I try to control mine. . . ."

"And I don't. . . ." To her horror she watched him move with the quick liquid grace of a tiger's spring across the distance that had separated them. She was just rising when he caught her to him, pushing her with gentle firmness back onto the couch and following her down. "You little fool . . . You haven't the slightest idea what you do to me. Your flame-gold hair, your exquisite beauty, your gentle innocence . . . And you accuse me of having no control, of being a man governed by only the basest instincts. What do you know of men, or of me?"

Blood pounded against her temples at the fierce passion in his voice. His intoxicating presence evoked primitive longings that almost destroyed her anger against him.

His large brown hands tenderly curved around the slender column of her throat, and he lowered his lips and kissed with studied deliberateness the exact spot where her pulse throbbed.

"I know that you are utterly ruthless," she began in a tremulous whisper, trying to ignore the hot tingling sensation his lips on her flesh evoked. "You will do anything—however unscrupulous—to get what you want."

He lifted his lips from her throat, but she could still feel his breath—warm and moist—as it fanned her skin. "What have I done that makes you think I'm ruthless?"

"For one thing . . . in Paris . . . you forced me . . ."

"All I did was kiss you."

"It w-was more than a kiss."

"In what way?"

She reddened under his level gaze. "I think you intended much more than a mere kiss."

"Perhaps—at first—but if I did, it was because at that time I thought you were the type of woman who expected it. After all, you came into my room and slipped into my bed wearing almost nothing. I ask you: What would any man think such a woman wanted?"

"I think you enjoy twisting things to make me look terrible. What I did was perfectly innocent."

"And when I realized that—haven't I tried to treat you with respect?"

"Yes, but I saw your true colors. I know the real you—what you're capable of."

"I've explained all that until I'm sick of it," Alexander snapped. "I've tried to convince you . . ."

"Convince me? Of what? Look what you've done now. You've brought me up here—we might as well be cut off from the rest of the world. I couldn't possibly escape if you tried . . ."

His expression hardened. "So you don't believe I brought you here to show you my collection of antiquities and the view—that this was a friendly gesture, rather than . . ." When she shook her head, he continued grimly. "You think I brought you here to seduce you—n-no, to rape you. I can see you've never gotten over your first impression of me—that I'm a criminal or at least that I have the tendencies to be one. I suppose I dismissed my servants so there could be no witnesses and then I brought you up to my bedroom with only one thing on my mind?"

He looked so fierce that she was truly frightened.

"Something like that," she said, proud of herself for not flinching.

"If I told you that my servants always take Saturdays off because I like to have the house to myself one day a week, and that I brought you here because I thought you'd enjoy the view and we could talk, you wouldn't believe me?"

"No. I wouldn't."

"Then no matter what I do, I'm damned in your eyes." When she did not deny this truth, a dark light flickered in his eyes. "Then I might as well take matters into my own hands."

His arms slid around her, imprisoning her.

"Alexander . . . no!"

But even as she made this demand, he was lowering his lips to hers, pulling her body more closely against his.

And when his mouth touched hers, she was lost in the destroying fire of his embrace. A low moan of ecstasy shuddered through her as he parted her lips with skillful ease.

She was aware of every place that his hard, muscled body touched hers. When he lifted his mouth from hers, his black eyes roved over her in a penetrating gaze. The lines beside his lips deepened, and she realized with dismay that he knew exactly how much she wanted him.

"You say 'no,' but your body says 'yes,'" he taunted. "Which am I to believe?"

Before she could reply, he said, "For all your innocence, you would be an easier conquest than most women."

Her cheeks warmed in a furious blush. "That's not true!"

"Oh, but it is." His slashing dark brows arched mockingly. "But perhaps you're only denying it because you would enjoy further proof." ·

He caught the slender hand that reached up to slap him, and bent his face to hers. Panic screamed through her as he smothered her cry with another kiss. ,

Another conquest! That was how he regarded her. But again her resistance flowed out of her and passionate longing for him pounded through her veins, proving the correctness of the statement he had made.

She felt herself drowning in a sea of conflicting emotions: anger, humiliation, desire, and frustration.

To her stunned amazement, he released her and drew in a deep, long breath, as if he sought to control the emotion driving him.

"One of us is crazy," he murmured unsteadily at last.

"It's definitely me," she responded in a tiny shaken voice. "How can I . . . I feel this way . . . when I know the kind of man you are?"

"And what kind is that?"

"Determined, egotistical, ruthlessly selfish . . . You'd say anything, do anything, hurt anyone to get what you want, wouldn't you? You think you're so attractive and rich you can have any woman. Yet you don't care for them in any deep way that lasts. Each girl is like an addition to your collection of conquests. You only want them to amuse you in bed until you tire of them."

"And what makes you so knowledgeable about the women in my life . . . and how they amuse me . . . in bed . . . until I tire of them?"

"I know your *type*."

"How do you know my type? How would you know what any type of man was like in bed? From your vast experience?"

She brightened in embarrassment. "Of course not."

"Then exactly what is the basis of your prejudice against my 'type,' as you put it, and our habits . . . in bed?"

The memory of her mother's heartache at the hands of such a man fleetingly raced through her mind.

"I want to go back to the hotel. You can't keep me here and force me to answer your ridiculous questions."

"Why can't I?" he growled, his lips curving into a mirthless smile. "A minute ago you accused me of bringing you up here with the purpose of forcing you to submit to me in bed. Surely such a dastardly fellow wouldn't think twice of forcing you to answer a question or two."

"Alexander Marianatos, I have no intention of telling you how I formed my opinions—but your actions tonight are evidence that I was right about you all along! The first night I met you, you would have raped me if . . ."

"How can you account for the miracle that I didn't?"

"I . . . don't know . . . I mean . . ." What was the use? He was a master at the art of twisting things around. She knew what he was like. Perhaps he could fool some women by confusing them, but not her.

"I kissed you, woman! For heaven's sake! That's hardly rape!"

"And tonight . . . you were charming—when we

ate and danced. I was almost convinced . . . until you brought me up here."

"And what have I done up here? I showed you the view. I kissed you again . . . after *you* provoked me to it."

"So I'm to blame for what you just did!" she cried out.

"In a way."

"Oh . . . you are impossible! You twist everything until I'm thoroughly confused."

"I'm about to decide that's your natural mental state," he commented dryly.

"Take me home—please."

"You're asking me—the type of man you despise, a veritable demon—to escort you home like a gentleman —before I've had my way with you?" he asked in mock seriousness. He buried his face in her hair. "Helen, this is the most absurd quarrel I've ever had with anyone. Perhaps we should start over, and I'll produce a set of character references."

"Let me go!"

"No! Apparently the only effective means of communication between you and me is physical."

He was smiling, a new fire kindled in his eyes. She knew that this time—once his lips claimed hers—there would be no stopping him.

She had to stop him—now!

"Alexander . . . I would like that drink you offered me a while ago. . . ."

"What?"

"I really am thirsty. . . ."

"Another Coke?"

"Yes."

Slowly he arose, his fingers combing the tumbled darkness of his hair, and went to the bar. His back was to her, and he didn't see her slip quickly into the bedroom and then out once more, elevator key in hand. The music whispering through the loft concealed any sounds she made.

With shaking fingers she inserted the key into the lock of the elevator and the doors opened noiselessly. She stepped inside. The doors were just shutting when Alexander glanced up from the bar, a look of stunned surprise on his darkly handsome face.

Once downstairs, she raced out of the house, past the Rolls, and down the drive to the gates that locked her inside his estate.

Desperately, she was wondering how she could escape when the deep, resonant tones of Alexander's voice behind her chilled her.

How had he gotten down so quickly? But of course— he had another key! Losing all hope, she turned to face him.

"Helen, why did you run away?"

"As if you don't know."

"For all the good it will do, I had no intention of seducing you—an innocent woman, a virgin. I wanted to kiss you, that's all. The irony is—you want me, too. But you have convinced me that you are determined to leave—Greece and me. I'm ready to drive you to your hotel."

The silence in the speeding Rolls was strained during the long drive back to downtown Athens.

When they reached her hotel, he handed her his engraved business card. "If you change your mind about staying, you can reach me at one of the numbers on this card."

"There's absolutely no chance of my changing my mind, or of you forcing me to do so," she protested quickly.

Piercing black eyes narrowed on her. "Is that a challenge?" he queried lightly, but his words hung in the air before she let herself out.

"Good night, Helen," he said softly after her.

Her heart seemed to stop beating at the finality she heard in his voice.

"Good-bye . . . Alexander . . ."

Chapter Five

The scent of shish kebab sizzling on the fast-food grill at the airport was more than Gary could stand.

"Helen, you hustled me out here with forty-five minutes to spare. You wouldn't even let me go down for breakfast. . . ."

"You were the one who overslept, remember? And I didn't want to take a chance on being late for our flight."

"Well, we're not late, so you can simmer down. I'm starved. You know I missed supper last night."

Helen was sure Gary was starved, and the shish kebab did look delicious.

"You can go on down to the gate with our tickets, and I'll be down in five minutes," he promised. When she dubiously lifted her brows Gary said, "I swear! I don't want to miss the flight any more than you do!"

The airport buzzed like a giant beehive. People swarmed everywhere—the sounds of their bustling footsteps and passionate voices mingling into cacophonous thunder.

Helen's thoughts turned from her brother to the tall, darkly handsome man who'd inhabited her dreams when she'd managed to sleep last night. She moved through the flowing crowd toward the gate mindless of everything, save one fact—she was leaving Athens, and Alexander, forever.

Her lightly applied makeup did little to conceal the pale blue shadows beneath her eyes or her hollow, lost expression.

She should be wildly happy that it was over between them, that she was free of him—but her heart dictated differently.

A short, fat man jostled heavily into Helen, forcing her thoughts away from Alexander. Losing her balance in the crowded corridor of the airport, she fell heavily against an enormous sign, knocking it over. The man scurried past her, obviously in too much of a hurry to help her.

Repositioning the fallen sign which translated into four languages, she read threatening bold orange letters: WARNING. RESTRICTED AREA. KEEP OUT.

Beyond she saw several guards standing before the closed door of a lounge.

Her own possessions had scattered across the concrete floor. Her purse had overturned, spilling its contents.

Suddenly, one of the armed guards strode toward her and, swooping down to his knees, began to assist her. Shakily, she stood up and brushed the dust from her skirt as he handed her her things.

"Thank you so much for your trouble," she responded graciously when he had given her everything.

His broad smile told her that although he didn't speak English, it was more pleasure than trouble to help so beautiful a woman.

Waving a grateful good-bye, she hurried on her way and he shouldered his long rifle and resumed his post.

"I can't even walk through an airport because of my

schoolgirl crush on an impossible man," she thought aloud.

Alexander . . . Every time she thought of him, she was aware of a tight ache in her chest. She must stop thinking of him . . . at once. . . . He had probably already forgotten she existed.

A quarter of an hour later found Helen mildly anxious as she searched the hordes of brightly dressed tourists pouring through the airport passenger lounge for any sign of Gary as she stood in the long line at the boarding gate.

"Miss . . . your passport and ticket, please. Miss . . ."

"Oh . . ." She hadn't realized she was at last at the front of the line. Quickly she handed the bored, olive-skinned girl behind the airline counter her passport and ticket, and those of Gary, also. "My brother, Gary, will be here any minute," she explained.

"Do you want smoking or non-smoking seats?"

"Non . . ."

The girl scribbled seat assignments and Helen gathered her purse and overnight case and headed for a chair in the passenger lounge.

Ten minutes ticked by—and still no Gary. What could be taking him so long?

All the passengers except Gary seemed to be present. Her head was beginning to pound, and she reached in her purse for an aspirin. She hadn't slept well last night. Her date with Alexander had upset her and left her depressed.

The roar of the airport did nothing to help her headache.

If only Gary would appear, she could relax!

At just that moment the loudspeaker blared and Helen strained to catch a woman's voice announcing first in Greek and then in English the departure of her flight to New York. Passengers rose and began to file out of the lounge.

Soon she was the only one who hadn't boarded, and Gary still wasn't there!

Adrenaline charged through her as she stared at the empty lounge in disbelief. She should never have left him by himself! But at the time it had seemed the rational thing for her to check them in while he ate.

Again the loudspeaker, announcing the final call for her flight, interrupted her thoughts.

What was she going to do? Outside the lounge, people, oblivious to her problem, still scrambled past. Although people were everywhere, she'd never felt so alone. There was no one to help her.

She knew no one in Athens except . . . Alexander.

She could do nothing but wait, and hope that Gary would suddenly appear.

Seconds passed like hours and she realized with a sinking heart that something very terrible must have happened to Gary for him to miss the flight.

She watched in a state of numb fear as her plane taxied down the runway and rose into a clear blue sky without them. . . .

Tense with desperation, Helen had enlisted the help of airport officials to search for Gary. When three hours had passed and he still could not be found, her nerves had been raw. One particularly kind official had rebooked her room at her hotel for her and told her to return to the hotel and wait for them to contact her there.

"I can't go back to the hotel . . . not knowing what has happened. Don't you understand? He's my brother!" she'd cried unreasonably.

"But there's nothing you can do for him by exhausting yourself here. Believe me, we'll find him," the man had insisted kindly.

But they'd already searched for three hours and they hadn't found him! her brain screamed. She'd lost all confidence that they ever would.

Overriding all her protests, the man summoned a taxi and gave the driver the address of her hotel.

The drive to her hotel did nothing to settle Helen's overwrought state of mind. The taxi careened through the kamikaze traffic as though it were driven by a madman. The downtown streets were choked with cars and buses and their fumes, and Helen's driver was constantly shouting abusive language and honking at other drivers who were all behaving in the same fashion.

Ahead of them a gleaming glass building slashed upward through sound and smog.

Alexander's building!

A plan began to form in her mind, causing her heart to beat faster.

He was up there! He was a powerful man, a man who could do anything he was determined to do, the very man who could find out what had happened to Gary—if she could only persuade him to.

But did she dare go to him? She remembered last night and how close she had come to giving in to him. Part of her had wanted to remain in Greece with him to grow to know him, to enjoy the fulfillment of his physical love. She'd cried herself to sleep telling herself over and over that she was right to go—that it would be wrong, and stupid, to do anything else. He would quickly tire of her, while her own feelings for him would deepen.

She was in turmoil. Why was it that just the thought of him did that to her?

The streets were jammed. The bumper of the taxi

behind them collided with their own, causing the driver's *komboloia*, bright red worry beads, that were attached to the rearview mirror, to swing madly. Helen was thrown violently forward against the front seat.

The driver muttered something fierce before turning around to see about Helen.

"I'm fine . . . really . . . but . . . I've decided you can let me out here," she assured him shakily.

"We're a mile from your hotel."

"That's all right." She handed him five hundred drachmas.

"Miss, for this I take you all the way to the hotel. The bump in the back is no reason to be scared. It happen every day. The traffic always is like this."

"It's not the bump in the back," she said, gathering her belongings together. "I've changed my mind about going to the hotel for now." Again there was a faint tremor in her voice as she apprehensively stole a glance upward at the soaring glass skyscraper.

Alexander! To see him again! A strange excitement coursed through her . . . but that was only because she was so worried about Gary and her own ability to persuade Alexander to help her find him.

As she marched through the glass doors of *his* building, the thought came to her: Would Alexander see this as an opportunity to achieve what he'd failed to achieve last night?

"I'm sorry, Miss," Alexander's smartly beautiful, black-haired secretary said firmly. "Mr. Marianatos left strict instructions that he does not wish to be disturbed. I'm holding all his calls." A manicured fingertip ran down a list of telephone numbers on the notepad by the telephone.

It was obvious the secretary considered the calls of

far more importance than the young woman who stood before her.

Desperation drove Helen to say, "But last night he promised me that . . . if . . . I stayed in Greece I could call on him . . . anytime . . . anywhere." From her purse she produced his engraved business card. "You see, he gave me all his telephone numbers."

The secretary fingered the card as her glance swept the woman before her with new interest. A tiny frown creased her lovely face as she studied Helen, carefully noting the prim, old-fashioned blouse and her brown-wren skirt. Clearly, she was puzzled, because Helen was not the sophisticated type of woman who usually called on Alexander.

But she kept her thoughts to herself, saying only, "I hope for your sake you are telling me the truth. He's not in the best of moods this morning, and he will be terribly angry if I call him out of this conference for nothing."

When the secretary left, Helen sat rigidly in a nearby chair to wait. She couldn't stop herself from fidgeting with the hem of her skirt, for she wasn't at all sure how Alexander would react to seeing her again.

A sound at the door warned her she was no longer alone. She looked up, startled—every nerve in her body aware of Alexander's magnetic presence. Her eyes met his intent, dark gaze, and her pulse accelerated. He stood in the doorway, lean and tall. He was elegantly attired in an expensive navy suit. She was dazzled by the sight of him, so masculine and totally virile.

His expression was deadly serious. The rumpled thickness of his black hair tumbled across his brow. He looked tired—as if, like her, he'd slept little the previous night.

But at the sight of her, his chiseled mouth quirked into that faint grin she was growing to love.

She returned his smile with a tender one of her own. It was so wonderful—seeing him again—that she felt strangely shy. Gary was forgotten, and there was only Alexander and her own leaping exhilaration to be with him once more.

As always, he seemed to sense her feelings, feelings that she wasn't able to openly admit to him. His wary look vanished. "Helen, darling, you've come back," he murmured huskily, no longer bothering to conceal his delight.

He'd called her "darling," and the sound of that endearment on his lips swept away her carefully organized speech. She could only stare blankly up at him with her heart fluttering erratically.

His black eyes seemed to pierce her very soul.

He thought she'd come back to him—to stay with him! And he was happy. She was so happy, too—just to see him once more—that she couldn't bear to spoil this moment by telling him the truth.

But she had to! "Alexander . . ." But the words wouldn't come.

Even before she tried again to frame the words to explain, he'd moved quickly with that smooth grace that was characteristic of him and wrapped her closely in his arms. His hands slid up the thin material of her sleeves, rustling it—warm, strong hands, expert in their touch. His voice was low and caressing. "Helen, I'm glad you're here. I haven't thought of anything but you since you left." He held her to him as if she were very dear.

Tell him! Tell him! Tell him! But she couldn't. His intoxicating presence overpowered her better judgment.

One of his arms went around her waist, and the other her shoulder, folding her so closely to him that she felt the taut muscles of his thighs against her own curving softness, the hard pressure of his coat buttons as they ground against her breasts. For a long time he just held her—silently.

Oh, he was too near! Dangerously so, and she couldn't think! All she could do was allow her body to melt against his. The pleasant scent of him enveloped her as he brushed a soft kiss into the thick silken gold that was her hair, his warm breath caressing her.

Deftly, his hand slid beneath the waistband of her skirt against her naked flesh to mold her hips even more closely to his.

Her body cried out for him, her desire greater than ever before—perhaps because last night she'd thought she'd parted from him forever.

She clasped her arms around his neck and moved one hand slowly through the thick, rich blackness of his hair. A low moan escaped her lips as she pressed the softness of her cheek affectionately against his own roughened one. This new tenderness on her part enflamed him, unleashing his tightly reined control.

"Oh, Helen, you are so, so beautiful."

His lips sought hers with possessive passion while his hands moved over her blouse to caress her breasts.

She felt light-headed—breathless. Was it always to be so when he held her? His tongue slid into her mouth against her own. His kiss destroyed all of her will against him, banished everything but her own need of him. There was an eagerness between them, an urgency, a new depth to their feelings that had not been there last night.

Slowly he withdrew his lips from her mouth to explore the creamy column of her throat.

He murmured against her ear, "I knew you had to realize we belonged together, darling. In a minute I'll call Georgios and have him drive you to the villa. You can rest, and I'll leave the office as soon as I can get away—in an hour or less—and we'll spend the rest of the day . . . and the night . . . together."

It sounded so wonderful, and yet . . .

Into her mind, swaying with desire, cold sanity returned. She had no intention of becoming his plaything.

He would have kissed her again, but she pressed two trembling fingers across his lips to prevent him from doing so.

She had to tell him the truth—before it was too late!

"Alexander . . . I-I didn't come back because I wanted to be with you," she whispered.

She felt the muscles of his body stiffen.

"Didn't you?" There was the faintest edge to his voice. His arms around her were as hard as steel.

"No . . ."

He drew in a deep, long breath, his black eyes boring through her, as though she were transparent. His expression was grim.

She was very aware of the sheer male size of him as he stared levelly down at her, aware of his overpowering virility and her own vulnerability to it. She would do well to remember her first impression that he was a dangerous man to toy with. Why hadn't she told him the truth in the beginning?

"Why did you come back, then?" he asked with deadly softness.

"Because I-I need your help."

"I should have guessed," he said with dry contempt. "Your passionate kisses were meant to persuade me to your cause."

"No, that . . . that's not true. I would never . . ."

"I'm beginning to realize that I don't know you at all," he muttered harshly, still refusing to release her. "What sort of help do you require—financial?"

"No, of course not."

His fingers tightened painfully on her upper arms as he observed her through the hooded sweep of his black lashes. His expression was controlled, but she knew he thought the worst of her—as he had the first night he'd met her.

"What *do* you want, then?" He spat out the question.

"My brother, Gary, is in terrible trouble. This morning . . . at the airport . . . he disappeared."

Slashing black brows arched with incredulity. "People don't just disappear. There must be a rational explanation. Did you consult with any of the officials at the airport?"

"Yes. . . . They searched for three hours. They're still searching. But they haven't found him." The combination of Gary lost and Alexander's increasingly harsh demeanor caused tears to form behind her lashes. She fought against the urge to cry.

"What do you want me to do that they haven't done?" he demanded, his manner softening a little.

"I want you to find him. Oh, Alexander, if you don't help me, I don't know what I'll do!"

"It strikes me as odd that you would come to me for help," he said, "when last night you said I was too ruthlessly selfish to think of anyone but myself."

"Alexander, last night I said a lot of things I didn't mean. I was angry. I felt trapped. . . ." A sob caught in her throat.

"In other words, as long as you need my help, you will refrain from such remarks, and you will endure my kisses. I see that, after all, you are not so different from the other women I've known." Contempt laced his deep, cold voice.

"Alex . . ."

Abruptly, he released his hold on her and ran his fingers through his thick hair. "Don't ever try to persuade me to do something for you by pretending feelings you don't have," he warned. "I prefer the truth—even when it's unpleasant. I'll help you—this once—because I'm a fool where you're concerned. But don't come to me again—ever—or you'll regret it."

The black, fathomless eyes that studied her belonged to a stranger, Helen thought with a shiver, realizing afresh how little she really knew about Alexander.

His threat echoed in her mind. Although his expertly tailored suit gave him a civilized appearance, it also emphasized the wild-animal grace and latent power of his muscular body as he moved beside her, ushering her from his secretary's office into his own grand suite.

"If I'm to help you, you must tell me everything that happened at the airport—no matter how irrelevant or insignificant," he said, his voice cool, his expression controlled.

Dominating the room was a magnificent desk embellished with gilt and inlaid marble that the Sun King himself would have been proud to own. An expanse of glass windows looked out upon the teaming metropolis sprawling beneath them.

He led her to a chair opposite his desk and then sat down himself behind it.

She told him everything she could remember while he made notes. When she finished, he said, "Something you said . . . about your fall . . . and those guards . . . clicks."

"But Gary wasn't even with me then. . . ."

"One of my associates at the conference mentioned

an announcement he'd heard over the radio. This morning an American was arrested in regard to an assassination attempt on a foreign dignitary at the airport. I'm wondering if this involves your brother."

"Gary's not that sort at all. He has no interest in politics."

Alexander was only half-listening to her. His large brown hand was knotted firmly beneath his chin, supporting it. His brows had drawn together in a pensive frown. She had the feeling his mind was working with computer precision.

Then his eyes flashed as he came out of his brief reverie and looked directly at her. "Helen, wait here. I'll cancel my conference and look into this matter concerning your brother—at once. You must understand—you could have a long wait. I have no idea where to begin this investigation. If you need anything just punch this buzzer, and my secretary will get it for you." He indicated his intercom with an offhand gesture of his wrist.

He was rising, and she realized by the prickle of anxiety going through her just how alone and insecure she would feel once he was gone.

"Alexander . . ."

He paused at the door, his expression impassive in spite of the plea he heard in her voice.

"Yes?" he replied coolly.

"I'm . . . afraid."

His frigid black gaze raking her with insolent appraisal sliced her emotions like a knife.

She was unaware of what the mute appeal on her lovely face did to him.

He muttered hoarsely. "Isn't it enough that I've promised to help you? Do you have to look at me like that?"

"How?"

"Don't pretend you don't know," he said, his voice rough with self-disgust, "exactly what you do to me when you give me one of those 'I'll melt if you touch me' looks." Dark anger hardened his features.

Then he was gone, his exit violent, although the door shut softly behind him.

The instant he was gone, Helen's mind flashed back to that first moment when he'd stood in the doorway of his secretary's office. He'd seemed very glad to see her, as if she meant more to him than a casual conquest.

Even when he'd thought she was using his attraction for her as a means to get him to find out what had happened to Gary, he'd agreed to help her in spite of his anger. Would he do that if he didn't feel something for her? Was she wrong about him?

Alexander's secretary entered the room, interrupting her thoughts.

"Mr. Marianatos sent me in to see if you needed anything."

"I-I'm fine."

"He's canceled his conference, as well as all of his appointments," the dark-haired girl said, clearly stunned as she looked at Helen with unabashed curiosity. "One of them was with a very important Soviet official."

"Alexander is helping me . . . solve a personal problem," Helen said, feeling she had to say something.

"Then I'm sure you'll have your solution quickly, for Mr. Marianatos will leave no stone unturned to help a friend."

Had she misjudged him?

Two hours passed before a grim-faced Alexander returned to his office.

The color draining from her face at the sight of him,

Helen half-rose from her chair. "Alexander . . . Gary . . . did you find out what happened to him?"

Alexander seated himself behind his desk. He saw her fear, and said quickly in soothing tones, "He's all right . . . physically speaking."

"What do you mean?"

"He's in jail."

"Jail!" The breath went out of her lungs with a gasp. "How? What happened?"

"I'm afraid this is a very serious matter," Alexander began gravely. "Your brother has been charged with the attempted assassination of an African prime minister."

"That . . . that can't be true."

"Nevertheless, it is," he assured her so seriously she could not doubt him. "This brother of yours has gotten himself into serious trouble." He leaned across his desk and inserted a crisp business card into her limp fingers. "You must make an appointment with this man. In fact, I'll have my secretary make it for you. He is an excellent attorney, and as a personal favor to me, he's agreed to represent you."

"I don't understand. None of this makes sense. Alexander, can I see Gary?"

"I've already arranged it—although even that was not easy. My chauffeur will drive you to the prison."

"Aren't you coming?"

"No!" He paused, anger hardening his features. "I think I've done more than enough for a woman who believes me to be a monster of selfishness. I've some pressing business problems of my own which I put off to personally conduct a two-hour search for your brother."

"Alexander . . ." She broke off. She could understand his anger. He thought she was using him. She wanted to apologize for what she'd said the evening before, but there was something so threatening in his expression that she could only say, "I do thank you . . . for everything. Y-you have been most generous."

She rose from her chair, and politely he got up from his, also, then escorted her to the door and opened it for her.

"I hope I won't have to bother you again," she said timidly. "I realize you're a very busy man."

"For your own sake, I hope you don't have to, either," he replied, a sardonic smile twisting his sensual lips. "Because, next time, my assistance will not be . . . free."

"But I'd be happy to pay you for what you've already done," she blurted out, not understanding his meaning.

"You owe me nothing for what I've already done." She was very aware of his eyes traveling from her face over her body. "But next time—if there is one—I will demand a price for my services."

Something about the way he was looking at her confused her.

"A price?" she questioned uncertainly.

"Surely you, an expert on my type, should be the first to understand, to expect it—from me. I find work—of any nature—dull without the incentive of profit. And you have something I want."

She couldn't resist the question. "And what is that?"

Again his eyes slid over her. This time he raised his hand to her chin and tilted it, as if she were a slave on the auction block and he a buyer inspecting the lovely merchandise. The hinted possession of his touch made her quiver.

"You . . . yourself . . . would be my price."

For a moment the air seemed electrically charged.

Warmth flamed through her. "Oh . . . Oh . . . I should have known better than to ask you. You see, I was right about you all along."

"Didn't I tell you once you were an excellent judge of character?" he asked. "You have my card. Call me if you need anything."

"You will be the last person I'll call—the very last!"

He laughed softly. "Will I? We'll see. Greek law is a labyrinth, and you may need an experienced guide to show you the way." His eyes roved over her possessively. "I'll be waiting to hear from you," he taunted before she turned to leave his office.

Chapter Six

Helen was oblivious to the Old World charm of her hotel room. Leaning forward in the large brass bed, she pressed the telephone receiver against her ear. Interference crackled, making it almost impossible to hear Hal's groggy voice.

"Come to Greece . . . now . . ." he muttered thickly, incredulous. "Baby, you're going to have to handle this one by yourself. You've got a good lawyer. I'll wire more money. . . ."

"Hal, don't you understand? Gary's in jail!"

"There's no way I can leave New York. I'm right in the middle of some very tricky negotiations."

Although they spoke for at least another minute, she could not persuade him to change his mind.

Dazed by her father's refusal to help, she hung up the phone. She slumped back against the thick pillows of her bed. Overhead, a ceiling fan lazily stirred the air. What was she going to do? Where could she turn?

Dino Athos, the lawyer Alexander had recommended, had been unable to obtain Gary's release. Delicate international politics were involved. To Helen's horror, he'd suggested she call Alexander back and request his help.

She could remember what he'd said almost word for word: "Miss Freeman, your friend, Alexander Marianatos, and a long-time client of mine, is one of the most powerful men in this country. If anyone can get your brother released, he can."

But she couldn't, she wouldn't, call him—not yet.

Weakly, she lifted the receiver once more and requested that the long-distance operator dial Bill Simpson. The sound of his voice was as calming as she'd known it would be until in his thorough, logical way he explained why he couldn't be of any help to her.

"Helen, there has to be someone in Greece you could turn to. Think," he advised coolly, rationally.

"I do know one man," she admitted in a small, defeated voice, as fear quivered through her like a whipcord.

It was late when she summoned the courage to call Alexander. His Greek housekeeper answered the phone, and then all too soon she heard the deep resonance of his voice on the line.

"Hello . . ." For a breathless moment she said nothing, and he repeated the greeting, this time faintly impatient. "Hello . . ."

"Alexander . . ." She tried to swallow to moisten her throat, which had suddenly gone dry.

"Helen, I've been thinking about you—wondering how things went today." He hesitated. "I was hoping you'd call."

Panic made her heart race wildly at the triumph she thought she detected in his voice. It was all she could do to control the impulse to slam down the receiver. But then, what of Gary? With nerveless fingers she gripped the black plastic receiver.

"Did you see your brother?" he queried, as if his interest were merely casual. The fact that she knew better caused her to swallow convulsively again.

"Yes, I saw him," she replied quietly.

"And what did Dino Athos advise you to do?"

Had Alexander deliberately sent her to a man he knew would send her back to him? At this thought a new emotion—cold fury—drove away her fear.

"You know exactly what he advised me to do!" she snapped.

"And what was that?"

"To call you."

For a long moment the only sound she heard was the desperate thudding of her own heartbeat.

Then he responded dryly, "You make it sound like a fate worse than death."

To be in the power of such a man!

Suddenly, because she could not stop herself, she burst into tears. "D-don't think for a minute I would call you if I could think of another way to help Gary," she sobbed brokenly.

There was a new hardness in his voice when he spoke again. "The situation is that desperate, then?"

"Mr. Athos can't do a thing," she said, regaining some of her control. "The charges against Gary are very serious. The authorities believe they have a tight case, and they won't listen to anything Gary and I say."

"You still believe Gary is innocent?"

"I know he's innocent! Before today he never even heard of the man they're accusing him of attempting to assassinate!"

"And so . . . you are willing to do anything to save your brother?" Alexander asked, his deep voice feather-light, yet vaguely threatening. "Even come to me for help—a second time?"

Blood pounded through her arteries. "Y-yes."

"Where are you?"

She hesitated briefly. "At the Grande Bretagne." She gave him the room number.

"I'll come at once."

She listened to his words—pleasantly low-pitched and vibrant—and reacted to them with the deadly calm of a condemned man hearing himself sentenced unjustly to a lengthy prison term. When he hung up, she scarcely knew that he did so.

She would have to bathe and dress before he arrived. Remembering the long drive from his villa to her hotel, she knew she had plenty of time.

Glossy white tile was cool against the feverishly warm flesh of her bare feet as she padded across the bathroom floor to run water into the tub. Her faded blue robe fell to her ankles in a rumpled pool and she stepped over it and into the tub. Absently, she sprinkled bubble bath into the flow of water.

He would be here soon, and this time everything would be different.

Strangely, on a conscious level she no longer felt apprehensive. The decision had been made. She had no choice but to pay his price for the sake of her brother.

She lingered in the tub longer than she should have. A curious lethargy possessed her. It was as though every nerve in her body had gone dead, and even though she knew she should get out and dress, she couldn't make herself do it.

A loud knock, reverberating against the bathroom door before it opened, shocked her back to reality.

Alexander Marianatos stepped inside. Negligently, he lounged against the doorway. His brilliant, intent gaze warmed her like a low fire in spite of the cool air seeping in from the bedroom with him.

"Alexander!" His unexpected and disturbing presence in her bathroom startled her and made logical thought impossible. She tried to disappear beneath the bubbles. "What are you doing in here?"

"Remember . . . you invited me." His fingers were loosening the knot of his silk tie; all too soon it was swinging free before he tossed it to the floor on top of her robe.

"Not into my bathroom," she replied, attempting to sound stern.

"I knocked outside ten minutes very properly." She was scarcely listening; instead, her attention was glued to the deft movements of his fingers, unbuttoning his shirt—slowly, button by button. Each button parted, exposing more bronzed skin. "Finally, I told the maid I was your husband, and I was worried about you. She let me in."

"Liar . . ." The word was no more than an accusatory whisper. "How could you . . ."

"Only partly. I *was* worried when you didn't answer. I had to think of some way to get in . . . and make sure you were all right."

His shirt, hanging unbuttoned, revealed a vertical strip of lean, muscular torso, tanned teak-brown.

Helen looked quickly away to avoid the force of his male presence. She felt ashamed she was not impervious to the sight of him like that. Her breath seemed to catch in her throat.

"Alexander . . . what . . . w-what are you doing?"

"No more games, Helen. You were willing enough this afternoon to respond passionately to me—when you wanted to persuade me to help you. What's the difference now?"

With one swift movement he shrugged out of his shirt. She was terribly aware of him as a man, of his lean, hard virility.

"N-no . . . P-please."

His shirt fell to the floor beside her robe and he

stepped over them as he walked casually to the edge of the tub.

His fingers were at the buckle of his belt.

"Alexander! No! Don't!"

"There's no reason to panic," he said smoothly. "You're doing the right thing. For all your hesitation and denial, you want me as much as I want you."

In a way what he said was true; furthermore, she'd agreed to a relationship with him for the sake of her brother. It was only natural that he now expected her compliance.

He knelt to her level and smoothed her hair back from her face.

Thinking that this was wrong no matter how much they wanted each other, Helen steeled herself against his touch.

His hand slid beneath her hair at the nape of her neck, and slowly he drew her face to his, his mouth claiming hers in a deliberately long kiss.

"I'll make you happy, Helen. I promise. "

His nearness, his touch, and his words evoked a response that was both ecstasy and torment. She realized suddenly she could love this man if circumstances were different—if he were different. But in that moment she almost hated him for the power he had over her, and for the fact he had the dishonorable intention of wielding his power.

"Alexander, how can we ever be happy if we do this?" she began shakily. "Do you think I could ever respect you or myself again? You're buying me—not with money, but with your power to help me." A terrible pain constricted her throat.

His fingers, at the back of her neck, tightened. "If I'm buying, then you, my noble little one, are selling," he said, his voice soft, yet harsh.

"Because I'm desperate! Don't you see the difference? I have nowhere else to turn. You could have my brother released, if you only would. I'm begging you."

"I don't want you to beg me. I want you to . . ." He bent lower, his dark, blazing eyes on her fearful face.

"N-no, Alexander. P-please . . . Don't do this. Human relationships should not be bought and sold. You may be in the habit of buying your women . . . but I . . ."

He muttered a fiercely hoarse oath beneath his breath as he jerked his hand from her neck. "Regardless of what you think, I've never paid any woman for sex," he declared angrily.

"Then don't start now," she pleaded, "expecially not with me."

"Why should you be special?" he retorted with disparaging cynicism that brought the warm rush of color to her cheeks.

It was obvious to her he regarded her exactly as he had all the other women he'd known.

"Because . . ." She broke off.

"You think I should help you for nothing?"

"Why not?"

His eyes gleamed strangely. "Because I'm not that kind of man, remember? You know all about me—my type." His low voice was savage. "I take what I want without regard to who might be hurt."

For the first time it occurred to Helen that she might have been unfair. "I should never have said those things."

"Why not, if you meant them? Do you regret them because you cannot wind me around your little finger as you would like to?"

"N-no." If only she could find the right words to convince him! "I realize now that I had no basis for any of those things I said. I was unfair. Your secretary told me this afternoon that you were very helpful—to your friends. And you have been very helpful to me. I don't know what I would have done without you."

He was listening to her seriously; he no longer seemed so angry. She continued, encouraged: "I'm sorry, Alexander, for what I said last night. Please . . . you must believe me."

His bold black eyes lazily raked her, and she was very afraid the thinning bubbles left little to his imagination. But if he liked what he saw, he gave no indication. Instead, he emitted a heavy sigh, picked up her robe, and placed it on the edge of the tub. "Get out and dress," he commanded tersely. "We'll talk. "

Only when he, shirt and tie in hand, had left did she emerge trembling from the tub. Slowly, she buttoned herself into her faded robe.

When she came out of the bathroom, he was fully dressed and sitting on a chair across from the bed. His gaze flicked briefly to her.

"Tell me everything that happened today," he said quietly.

She sat down upon the bed and struggled to compose her thoughts. The quilted fabric of her robe brushed against her naked flesh. If only she were properly dressed, she might feel more at ease.

"Well, this morning Gary was running toward the gate where our plane was to depart," she began. "He was late because he'd stopped to help an elderly lady with her wheelchair."

"Yes."

"Somehow he wandered into a heavily guarded V.I.P. lounge. He didn't see the signs warning people away because the airport was so crowded and he was running. Everything happened with nightmare speed after that. As soon as he burst into the lounge, he was immediately surrounded by armed soldiers. Bayonets were poking into his stomach."

"I see. Not a very pleasant predicament for a sixteen-year-old," Alexander said sympathetically.

Because he was such a courteous listener, she no longer found talking to him so difficult.

"The soldiers searched him, and when they found a small knife he'd bought in a bazaar near Hadrian's Arch and had forgotten to pack, they were convinced he was guilty. You see, the man they were guarding is a controversial political figure from an unstable Third World country. There have been many threats against his life—one of them was made only yesterday.

"Besides the knife, do they have any other evidence against your brother?" Alexander asked.

"Not really. But when he couldn't produce his plane ticket or passport because I had them, they didn't believe him. When I told them this afternoon he was telling the truth, they wouldn't believe me, either. It seems that an American fitting Gary's description was seen with a group of political activists yesterday." She ended on a desperate note. "They're holding Gary without bond. He's going to have to stand trial."

Alexander frowned as though he were mentally going over everything that she had said.

"Don't you see? That boy with the political activists could have been anybody!" Helen blurted out in a passionate effort to convince him.

"Just as I see why the police feel justified in detaining your brother."

"You don't believe me?"

"I didn't say that."

"Will you help me?"

"Yes, I'll help you," he said slowly, his eyes going over her with a look of studious appraisal which made her flush hotly as she remembered that, except for her robe, she was naked. "For a price."

Her heart knocked frenziedly against her ribs.

"B-but I thought you said . . . a while ago . . . that you didn't buy women. . . ." She clutched the robe around her body.

"I don't. I have no intention of coercing you into a physical relationship with me in payment for your brother's freedom. But I do want you to stay here in Athens at my villa—with me."

"How long?"

"Until I decide you can go."

Helen gulped in a deep, quick breath. And she'd thought she'd been unfair in her judgment of him! Doubtless he had no intention of letting her go before he seduced her! How could any part of her respond to such a man?

"What will people think of our relationship? That I'm your mistress?" she demanded.

"I don't care what people think! But if it will make you feel better about your position, we will say that I've hired you as a secretary to help me when I work at home."

"And who would believe that? I'm a concert pianist. I can't even type."

"I couldn't care less."

No, because that was exactly what he wanted people to believe.

"You will keep me, until I give in to you, and you tire of my body."

His expression was as hard as granite as he expelled a deep, exasperated breath. "For an innocent girl, you come up with the ugliest notions."

"It's the truth!"

Angrily, he responded, "Perhaps."

"I hate you, Alexander Marianatos! I hate you!"

Black eyes danced across her face with knowledge-able insolence. "And do you kiss all the men you hate with such . . . ardor?" Heat rushed through her veins as he continued with infuriating blandness. "But your feelings for me are hardly the issue. Do you or do you not want your brother released on bond?"

She hesitated for a long time, struggling to suppress her fury. "You know I do."

"Then I suggest that you begin packing at once," he drawled, his deep voice cold with contempt.

She regarded him with defiance for a long moment— her eyes darkly blue—before she realized the futility of opposing him.

She was completely in his power, and he knew it.

Morning sunlight filtered through silken draperies and bathed the suite of rooms Alexander had given her with its golden warmth. The understated elegance of the vast bedroom, sitting room, and bath, all decorated in the softest shades of blues and yellows, all reflected money. But for all its beauty, the room was a prison, Helen thought dismally as she folded the pillow beneath the thick satin coverlet of her bed.

Casting one last look at herself in the floor-to-ceiling mirror and repinning a tumbling lock of gold hair back into the tight knot at the back of her neck, she decided she was ready to go down for breakfast. She was again wearing her brown shirt and lacy, old-fashioned blouse because she had no other clothes in her overnight case. Although neither her drab clothes nor her severe hairdo flattered her, neither did they conceal her beauty.

A faint smile of triumph tugged at the corners of her lips as she examined her gold watch. Nine-thirty A.M. Alexander would have left long ago for his office. She had deliberately arisen late to avoid him.

As she descended the swirling staircase into the grand salon, Maria, Alexander's middle-aged housekeeper, greeted her warmly.

"Good morning, Kiria. Kirie Marianatos is waiting for you on the terrace by the pool." A plump arm waved her toward glass doors.

"He . . . is . . ." Shock momentarily prevented any further speech.

She stepped out onto the terrace. Stiff legs carried her toward the compelling figure, so totally male, sitting at a table set for two. A faint breeze curled the crisp white tablecloth and rustled the newspaper he was reading. The pale-smoke color of his elegant three-piece suit contrasted with his own dark coloring.

At the sound of her approaching footsteps, he looked up from his paper, a half-smile curving his hard mouth.

"Good morning, Helen," he said, politely rising to help her into her chair. "I hope your tardiness this morning is a result of your having slept well . . . your first night in my home."

His mocking tone was so infuriating that a dark flush crept from her neck upward, but she controlled the urge to lash back at him.

He turned from her and spoke rapid Greek to Maria. "I told her to bring our breakfast," he explained courteously.

As the woman disappeared, Helen wondered what the housekeeper must be thinking of her. Alexander had placed her in a very uncomfortable position. Helen's anger toward him intensified.

"Today I will subscribe to an English newspaper," he began. "I seem to remember it's your habit to read over breakfast."

"You needn't bother." She managed to speak calmly. "I won't be staying . . . that long."

"How do you know?" Forcing herself to meet the challenge of his bold black eyes for the briefest instant, she saw indomitable determination harden his lean features. "I, not you, will make that decision," he finished, flicking his paper to another page.

Maria served their breakfast, and they ate it in stony silence. With every bite Helen grew more furious at her own helplessness. She was completely in the hands of this man, a man who, she was beginning to realize, was utterly ruthless.

"Have you done anything to help free my brother?" she asked quietly.

"Not yet."

He picked up another section of the paper. His air of nonchalance toward her brother was more upsetting than anything else he'd done. She was determined not to let the matter drop.

"Why not?" There was a vaguely accusatory element in her soft question.

He looked up from the newspaper article he'd been reading. "If it were as easy to free him as you seem to think, you would not be here with me, now, would you?" He paused, studying her with his level gaze. "You could get him out yourself. Besides, there is no particular hurry. . . ."

No particular hurry! Would he feel that way if it were he who was rotting in prison? His indifference showed her how unspeakably cruel he could be.

"You are deliberately toying with me," she said, anguished.

"I thought I was reading the newspaper."

"You know what I mean."

"As a matter of fact, I don't. I was going to say that none of the people I need to contact are in their offices yet. I do not think it would help your brother if I pestered them at their homes."

"Oh, I hadn't thought of that," she said in a small voice.

"No, you are so certain that I am abominable that I

can get into trouble with you when I've done nothing but act in what I consider your best interests. You're so anxious for me to serve you. Yet what have you done for me?"

"All I expect is for you to be fair and show a little kindness to someone in trouble."

"As you have been fair and kind to me?" he asked ironically.

"That's different."

"In what way?"

"You know as well as I. You're twisting things around again to suit your own purposes."

Suddenly, his patience snapped. In one swift movement he rose, towering over her. He flung the newspaper to the table. His expression was fiercely condemning: his mouth had thinned to a hard line; his eyes blazed like two dark flames.

"I'm getting tired of your accusations and demands! I've decided it's about time I got something out of this arrangement," he declared savagely. "You can do something to please me."

"I'm living . . . with you."

"That's not enough."

She bit her bottom lip. She had known it would come to this! He was not the type of man who could be satisfied merely with a few kisses.

She felt the appraisal of his gaze sliding over her. To her amazement, he said only, "You can start by wearing your hair down again and removing that hideous skirt and blouse. If I ever see you wearing those clothes again, I will personally remove them."

The thought of him doing that evoked a treacherous thrill.

"But . . . I have nothing else to wear. My clothes are on the airplane. . . . Why, they're in the States by now."

115

"Still, if you're going to live with me, you will dress according to my tastes."

"I have no money for a new wardrobe to suit your tastes . . . and even if I had . . ." She swallowed the end of her sentence, remembering how futile it was to defy him.

But he had caught the edge of defiance in her voice, and it angered him. "Why do you insist on being the disagreeable spitfire? At last we've hit on what *you can do* for me. You can dress so that you look even more beautiful."

His authoritative tone ignited the fuse of her temper. "I won't do it!"

"You seem to have forgotten that you are living with me in payment for a debt—a fee for services. Nothing is being asked of you except that you please me. So far this morning you've been thoroughly disagreeable. You deliberately kept me waiting two hours." He spoke smoothly, but his penetrating gaze told her he hadn't been deceived about the reasons for her tardiness. "In the future you will be down here no later than seven-fifteen, or I will come up and get you myself." He went on: "It's time you learned I will call the shots, not you. If I say you wear a new wardrobe, then you will."

Helen listened to each word with growing resentment. When he finished, she swung herself quickly to her feet, her blue eyes as dark as navy. Clearly, he had every intention of treating her as a woman he kept for his pleasure. His high-handed treatment was insufferable, not to be borne.

"I-I . . ." She was trembling with agitation. "I don't have to endure this from you! I won't! I'm leaving!"

Slashing dark brows raised with cynical mockery. "Go right ahead," he returned with silky indifference.

She bolted from him, her high heels slapping like frantic heartbeats against the flagstones before she halted abruptly several feet from the tall glass doors. She turned back to look at him.

He stood motionless beside the table, the hard line of his mouth quirking with sardonic amusement as he observed her. There was a quality of arrogant mastery in both his expression and his stance that further maddened her. She realized with a start that he'd anticipated she'd think twice of her own hasty action. Even as she asked the question, she knew what he would say. "And Gary?"

"You know the answer to that. If you leave, you can see to his release yourself."

Slowly, her head slumping slightly in defeat, she retraced her steps and sank hopelessly once more into the chair opposite his.

"At least you are capable, however occasionally, of thinking rationally," he said coolly, his darkly handsome face a smooth blank as he again lounged back in his own chair. "I'll send my chauffeur for you at one this afternoon and meet you myself in the fashion district of Athens."

"You're coming!

"But of course. If I leave you to your own devices, you might select something as dreadful as that blouse and skirt you're wearing, as well as that robe you were wearing last night. I have no intention of wasting my money on clothes that don't enhance your beauty."

"Your money?" Her face went ashen with horror. "I couldn't possibly let you buy my clothes."

Helen was aware of Alexander's piercing black gaze narrowing on her features. She forced herself to meet it and was shaken by the ruthless determination she saw etched in the harsh planes of his face.

"Of course you can," he replied levelly, suave brutality in his voice. "Remember, in a sense, you belong to me now. You had better get used to that fact."

117

Languidly, he arose just as she sprang to her feet, a fiery anger burning through her. She would have run from him had he not seized her and pulled her hard against him. She writhed and twisted, determined to break free and run to her room, where at least she could be alone.

She struggled against him madly, but his embrace was like iron. At last she gave up and forced herself to passive stillness. For a long moment he held her, her face pressed so closely against his chest that she heard the fiercely irregular thudding of his heart."

"It doesn't have to be this way between us," he said softly at last, his lips descending to the hollow of her throat.

His hard, warm mouth against her flesh evoked an unwilling response. The anger she'd felt toward him dissolved; she trembled in his arms. His lips followed the curve of her neck and nuzzled the flesh beneath her ear, arousing treacherous sensations in her.

His seductive mastery left her weak-kneed and clinging to him. Only with the greatest effort did she manage to disengage herself from his arms.

Better anger than this overwhelming desire to give in to him and become just another of his women!

On shaky legs she ran from the terrace to the safety and privacy of her own room. She threw herself across her bed.

He had said she belonged to him, and he was right. But it was not he who imprisoned her, but her own undeniable desire for him. Now that she was to be exposed to his rugged virility on a daily basis, how long would it be before she became his in every sense of the word?

Chapter Seven

"But of course I will keep the shop open for you, Monsieur Marianatos. What is the importance of the siesta hour, when I can be of help to you?" the willowy Madame Moreau gushed as she welcomed Alexander and Helen into her posh boutique just off Kolonaki Square.

Graciously, Alexander took the woman's extended hand and pressed it to his lips. The gesture hinted at a former intimacy between them, and Helen felt vaguely annoyed. Nor was she able to ignore the beautiful French woman's warm response to his kiss.

Madame Moreau led them to a luxurious sofa. "I have given our telephone conversation of this morning much thought, Monsieur," she purred. Her golden eyes skimmed Helen in quick appraisal. "And now that I have see your . . . friend . . ."—the soft irony in the sophisticated voice knotted the muscles in Helen's stomach—". . . I think I have exactly what you require. If you will be seated, my models will soon be ready to begin."

"I would prefer to have my friend model what you have selected, Françoise," Alexander commanded.

"Naturellement," Madame Moreau acquiesced.

A furious blush suffused Helen's cheeks as she rose to follow Madame Moreau to the dressing room.

Some of Madame Moreau's selections were outrageous. *Harem glamor* she had called one creation. The blouse was all ruffles and flourishes. Harem pants were poufs of flaming organza that gathered in jeweled cuffs at Helen's slender ankles.

Alexander rejected this creation and chose, instead, sytles which were simple, yet stunning. The last dress Helen modeled was a black cocktail gown. Its neckline plunged between her high, firm breasts; the soft, clinging fabric of the skirt had been slashed to show off her shapely legs. The dress was so revealing she felt almost naked in it.

He was looking at her in the gown—his darkly intense gaze moving over her body was like an abrupt physical impact. For one long moment their eyes met. She saw the frank admiration in his, and she knew he found her desirable. Excitement tingled through her. Now she wondered about the easy familiarity between Françoise and Alexander. Painfully, she asked herself: Had they once been lovers? Or had they grown acquainted because it was Alexander's habit to bring his mistresses here to buy their clothes?

When Helen returned to the main room of the salon dressed once more in her old clothes, Alexander said, "But you aren't through modeling, my dear."

"Madame Moreau told me that was the last dress," Helen retorted icily.

"The last dress . . . yes. But we haven't selected any . . . intimate apparel." His black eyes gleamed with impertinence.

Lingerie! Enough was enough!

Parading before him fully dressed, his eyes boldly

roving over her with critical appreciation, had been dreadful. She couldn't possibly model filmy night clothes.

He was fingering a sheer white chiffon gown trimmed with silvery satin. The sight of such a feminine garment in so masculine a man's hands was unnerving. At the thought of modeling it for him, she caught her breath. Her pulse fluttered wildly.

"I won't model that!" she cried.

He held it up so that the gauzy material swirled to the floor. Why, she could see right through it! He flashed her a warm, knowing smile. "Why not? You would look beautiful in it." There was a hushed, intimate quality to the low-toned statement that flustered her.

"I-I won't," she persisted stubbornly, blushing deeply.

He tilted his black head back and regarded her, amusment quirking his mouth. She saw the bland mockery in his eyes that she dared to challenge his authority over her. Then he shrugged lazily. "All right. Much as I regret it, I suppose in this, I will allow you to have your way."

She could scarcely contain her fury that this man had such control over her.

Kara, the bright, vivacious upstairs maid, helped Helen unpack her new clothes.

"Kiria," the young girl bubbled with childlike pleasure as she pulled one gown after the other from the multitude of boxes littering the grand bedroom. "Each one is more beautiful than the last!"

Helen's own depression increased as she observed the maid's excitement. She sank down upon the bed. She herself could take no joy in something that represented her bondage to Alexander. At last she dismissed

121

the maid and spent the remainder of the day in her room. She tried unsuccessfully to read a magazine she'd purchased at the airport.

What was she going to do? She was terribly aware of the gilded clock above the carved mantel chiming the passing of each hour. All too soon it was time for Alexander to return from work, and she still had no solution.

She had to stay with him—because of Gary.

This realization was sinking into her brain when a brisk knock sounded upon her door.

"Come in," she called absently from her bed. She was half-expecting Kara.

"Good evening, Helen." The deep, familiar tones startled her, causing her heart to thunder in her chest. Her eyes met Alexander's too-knowing ones.

Tall and firmly built, he looked dashing in his impeccably elegant, pale-smoke suit. He flashed her a smile, and her gaze lingered on the hard, sensual curve of his lips before she forced herself to look away.

Oh, why did he have to have such a devastating impact on her senses?

He held a drink in one hand. "I see you haven't finished unpacking," he commented dryly, lifting his glass to his mouth.

"No, I haven't." She tried to make her voice sound sulky to discourage him.

He only ignored her marked lack of enthusiasm for the task, as well as for his own company. Moving toward her, he said, "Well, you can attend to that later. Kara will help you. Tonight we are having guests for dinner. You will act as my hostess."

"Your hostess! I don't even know the people you've invited."

"Nevertheless, I'm sure you won't refuse me. One of

the guests is a man who is in a position to help your brother."

"Oh."

"I've invited two Soviets, as well," Alexander continued. He was standing close, too close, to the bed.

"Have you obtained Gary's release?"

"Not yet . . . although I've been trying. The man I need to talk to is temporarily out of the country."

And ugly suspicion flared in her mind. She did not believe the man was out of the country. Alexander was only saying so to keep her at his mercy.

"I see you haven't changed your clothes," he said. A subtle inflection in his voice brought her sharply to attention.

"I saw no reason to," she managed to say calmly.

"Have you forgotten what I told you I'd do if I saw you wearing that again?" This time there was no mistaking the innuendo.

He towered over the bed. He'd said he'd remove them himself. "I'm beginning to think this is your way of inviting me to undress you," he persisted, leaning toward her.

"No, you wouldn't! You wouldn't dare!"

"Wouldn't I?" Swiftly, before she could slither across the satin spread to the other side of the bed, he caught her and pulled her hard against him. He set his drink down on the night table beside the bed. His strong hands fingered the thin fabric of her blouse as he traced a tingling path up the length of one sleeve. "Don't tempt me."

He tilted her chin with one of his fingertips so that she was forced to stare deeply into his eyes. His expression was so intense that her throat felt oddly tight. She breathed unevenly. So powerfully was she attracted to him that she wanted nothing more than for his lips to descend to hers. She longed to surrender to her desire and belong to him completely.

Yet, knowing the kind of man he was, she knew that to give herself to him would be a terrible mistake. It would only enable him to hurt her all the more ruthlessly.

She managed to tear her gaze from his handsome, bronzed face. "Let go of me," she hissed.

"As soon as you agree to change—both your clothes, and your hairstyle."

"I'm appropriately attired."

His strong fingers, at the collar of her blouse, were a potent reminder of how easily he could shred her blouse and made good his threat.

"I didn't spend a small fortune on your clothes so that I would have to continue looking at you in that. It is very important to me that tonight you dress glamorously," he said in a dangerously quiet voice.

Abruptly, he released her, then went to her closet. After rummaging through her newly purchased wardrobe for several minutes, he pulled out a low-cut evening gown of vivid blue taffeta.

"You will wear that," he commanded, "if I have to dress you in it myself."

And he would do just that! As he advanced upon her, the bright dress slung carelessly over his arm, his dark eyes gleamed with determination.

"All right! All right!" she acquiesced just before he reached her. "I'll wear it!"

"I thought you would," he taunted softly, "when you had time to reconsider. To tell you the truth . . ." He paused as his gaze swept over her, causing her to flush with fury. "I almost regret your decision." His triumphant, mocking smile—white against his bronzed skin —further inflamed her.

Inwardly, she raged because of her helplessness. But

she contained her anger and only stared after him in frozen silence as he stalked across the thick carpet and left the room.

Helen found Alexander in the library going over some papers he'd brought home with him. For a moment she observed him without him knowing that she did so.

The thick waves of his jet-dark hair gleamed like black satin beneath his reading light. Disturbingly handsome in his elegant evening clothes, he looked preoccupied. Briefly, Helen wondered what was worrying him before he looked up and saw her.

Quickly, his dark gaze ran over her in sweeping assessment. She was swathed in tightly fitting blue taffeta, as he'd demanded. But the lines between his slashing brows creased slightly at the sight of her hair, still primly arranged in a knot. A dark, challenging light flashed in his black eyes as he rose and came toward her.

"Ever the little rebel," he said softly. "When will you learn that it is useless to fight me?"

She did not resist him when he placed his hands in her hair and removed the pins with expert ease. Flame-gold masses tumbled to her shoulders. He was looking at her with such admiration that she could not help gasping. At her first attempt to back away from his mesmerizing nearness, his large tanned hands spanned the naked flesh of her back where her cocktail gown had been cut away. The touch of his fingers was fire. Then he pressed his lips into the abundant flowing ripples of her hair just as a servant entered to announce the arrival of their dinner guests. Abruptly, he released her.

That evening, as she sat across the gleaming length of the fabulously appointed dinner table from Alexander, she again pondered the hopelessness of her situation. Throughout the meal, Alexander largely ignored her, concentrating instead on the two officials from the Soviet Union, who sat beside him. The other guests were Greek businessmen. Which one in particular was the man who could help Gary, she did not know. She was the only woman present. Again she wondered why Alexander had been so insistent that she act as his hostess.

From time to time she grew aware of the speculative glances the two Soviets occasionally cast in her direction. What must these dinner guests be thinking of her? Alexander had introduced her as his secretary, but she was dressed in a designer gown no secretary could afford. Were they wondering about her relationship with Alexander? Or did they assume she was his mistress? She noted that the Greeks treated her deferentially, as though they were accustomed to dining with Alexander's mistresses. Was it his habit to have his women act as his hostesses?

Dinner was over, and as Alexander drew back Helen's chair to escort her to the salon, where they could converse more comfortably, the fat blond Soviet stared at them hard, a lewd gleam lighting his watery, blue eyes. It was all too clear what he was thinking. Helen reddened with shame. She couldn't endure this! Not for another minute!

She pressed shaking fingers to her temples and, pleading a headache, begged Alexander to excuse her. Reluctantly, he did so.

The stiff skirt of her tavetta gown swishing, she left Alexander laughing and conversing with his guests over after-dinner drinks. Glancing at her watch, she saw that it was the perfect hour to call Bill Simpson and tell him she was breaking her teaching contract to remain in

Greece. If she called him now, she could catch him before he left for work. Because Alexander was occupied, she could be assured of privacy.

The overseas operator had difficulty placing the call, and Helen was forced to wait nearly an hour. She passed the time in Alexander's library reading. At last the call went through.

After she'd told Bill her news, there was a long moment of strained silence. Then Bill said, "I don't understand. If you expect Gary to be released very quickly, why are you staying?"

Helen trembled slightly. The urge to confide her problem was very strong, but it wouldn't be fair to burden dear, gentle Bill. What could he—so far away—do, anyway, against a man like Alexander?

"Bill, I can't explain."

"It's obvious you haven't received my letter telling you about the concert tour I've arranged for you this fall."

"Oh, no!" she cried out, feeling acute disappointment at the thought of canceling the tour. "You'll have to cancel it," she finally said in a flat, toneless voice.

"But Helen, I was so looking forward to seeing you."

In her softest voice, she replied, "I was looking forward to seeing you, too, Bill. . . ."

As she placed the receiver back on the hook, the library doors closed so savagely she was startled. "Alexander . . . I thought you were entertaining your guests."

His face was dark with anger. "Obviously. You left me and my guests so you could sneak away and talk to your Bill."

"I did not!" she denied hotly, angry because of the canceled concert tour.

He moved nearer. In spite of his elegant evening

clothes, she was very aware of him as a man—primitively male, powerfully dangerous.

"You had no right to come here, to spy on me, to eavesdrop!" she flared.

"Fool that I am, I came to see about you. I thought you were ill."

"Oh . . ."

"Are you in love with him?" Alexander demanded curtly.

Why did she feel on the defensive? Alexander was the one who was keeping her here, forcing her to cancel a concert tour she'd worked toward for years.

"If I had any sense at all, I would be in love with him or with someone exactly like him," she snapped, furious with him for being so unreasonable. "Bill's wonderful and gentle—not at all like you. Bill would never force me or any woman to . . ."

Her words were cut off as he swept her into the steel circle of his arms. "I've heard enough about your Bill," he growled. "I know how I can put him out of your mind."

Helen twisted frantically to escape the domination of his hard mouth descending to claim hers. Cruelly, his lips ravaged the softness of her own.

As her resistance drained from her, so did his anger. His arms about her loosened; the pressure of his lips on hers eased.

When she broke free of him, he did not try to restrain her. "Y-you had no right to do that," she said shakily.

"You have only yourself to blame—for taunting me with your words . . . and your beauty." His bold, insolent gaze swept to the spot where her partially bared breasts heaved above the sheen of vivid blue taffeta.

Flushing, she pulled up the fallen strap of her gown.

"I'm going to my room now—to be alone," she retorted haughtily. "And for your information, I intend to lock my door to keep out unwanted intruders!" She stared at him pointedly.

She was halfway across the room when his harsh laughter stopped her. "Do you, my little one—you who know my type so well—really think that if I were determined to have you, a locked door would keep me out?"

Later—even though it was no more than a defiant gesture—she did lock her door. But as she lay sleepless in her bed thinking of him, she wished it were as easy to lock him out of her heart and mind as it had been to lock him out of her room.

Even though Helen went downstairs before seven-fifteen the next morning, Alexander had arisen even earlier and gone to his office. She should have been thankful that she didn't have to face him, but as she stared at the empty wrought-iron chair opposite the table set solely for her, she experienced an acute sense of disappointment to have missed him, as well as a curious hurt that he'd deliberately left early to avoid her.

After breakfast, the day without Alexander stretched before her—long, empty hours that had to be filled. A feeling of intense restlessness possessed her, and she realized with a start it was a sign she was settling into Alexander's home as if she belonged there. She recognized the feeling for what it was—the need to practice. Always when she lived anywhere for any length of time, she spent five hours a day practicing her instrument.

She had been away from the piano for over a month. But she had been busy touring and worrying about

Gary. Now that she felt more relaxed, more *settled*, she naturally felt the need to work.

Instead of marveling that she actually was beginning to feel at home in Alexander's house and analyzing this change in herself, she told Maria she would like Georgios to drive her to a music shop she'd seen near Kolanaki Square.

Two hours later found her seated before the concert grand in Alexander's music room. She began her arduous technical exercises first before starting on the repertoire she'd been practicing for the past year.

She grew so engrossed in her music that the day passed quickly. Her fingers were rippling faultlessly through a crescendo of her favorite Chopin nocturne when a faint sound behind her broke her concentration and she paused.

"Don't stop because of me, Sis."

"Gary!" His name was a shriek of pure joy as she flung herself into the arms of the tall, lanky boy who was smiling at her affectionately. After a long moment she tilted her head back and studied him closely. "You're all right? They didn't hurt you?"

"Other than being starved, I'm fine," he said, grinning down at her."

Nothing else he could have said would have assured her more. If his voracious appetite was intact, he must be all right.

"Alexander has promised me a thick steak and baked potato tonight," Gary continued.

At the mention of Alexander, she drew back. She felt strangely expectant at the thought of seeing him again. "Where is . . . he . . . Alexander?"

"He said he'd go for a swim—to give us a chance to be alone together."

"I . . . I have to thank him."

"Why don't you put on your bathing suit while I

freshen up. I'll meet you at the pool in a couple of minutes," Gary agreed.

She flew to her room and changed quickly into the shiny, gold, one-piece bathing suit Alexander had bought for her. As she descended the stairs, the thought of seeing Alexander again aroused feelings that were inexplicably intense.

All day she had missed him, and now to discover that he had obtained Gary's release . . . It was only natural she should feel a deep sense of gratitude. Yet, was it only gratitude that made her pulse accelerate at the thought of seeing him again, that caused this fluttery thrill in the pit of her stomach?

When she reached the pool, Alexander was toweling himself dry. His rumpled black hair had a damp sheen to it. Weakly, she observed the fluid power of his lean, hard physique as he languidly sat down upon a chaise longue. She took a quick, deep breath at the sight of so much darly tanned, virile flesh.

She longed to apologize for the harsh words that had divided them.

Then he saw her, and the sensuality of his brief gaze sliding downward over her curves in the revealing bathing suit colored her cheeks with crimson. In her confusion she forgot what she'd intended to say.

"Helen"—the warmth in his voice radiated through her—"I enjoyed your playing earlier. It was very beautiful."

His words of praise illuminated her beautiful face. Shyly, she answered, "Thank you."

Did you enjoy your day?" he asked quietly, as though he really cared.

"Yes, I did." She did not tell him that she'd missed him, that she'd regretted their quarrel. There did not seem to be the need.

She had the strangest sensation that this was what it

could be like every day if he were her husband. How pleasant it would be to see the man one loved after a long day apart.

The man one loved! Was she in love . . . with Alexander? Was that why she was so intensely drawn to him?

She rejected the idea quickly. It wasn't possible! It wasn't! She was grateful to him and attracted to him physically, but that was all! She would not foolishly allow herself to fall in love with a man like him.

At just that moment Gary arrived. He dove into the pool, and Alexander, throwing his towel aside, joined him. The two engaged in rough horseplay—splashing and hollering. And Helen, watching them, realized that an easy familiarity already existed between them. She sprang into the pool herself.

Steaks were served on the terrace. Over dinner Helen discovered that Alexander had spent his entire day with Gary. After he'd obtained her brother's release, he'd brought him to his office, where the two of them had talked together for more than an hour assessing Gary's interests. When Gary had expressed enthusiasm for working on Alexander's maintenance crew, Alexander had hired him.

Gary was finishing his second steak as Alexander praised him for an air-conditioner repair he had done.

"Do you know, Helen, I think this brother of yours is a genius when it comes to machinery."

"Just don't let him near your car, or it will be in pieces," she warned, feeling unaccountably happy.

Gary was rising. "You've just reminded me, Sis. Georgios promised to let me take a look at the engine of that Rolls. . . ."

As he disappeared in the direction of the drive, Helen warned laughingly, "You'd better go with him, Alexander, if you value your automobile."

"I value your company more." Alexander's husky voice was low, intimate.

A prickly sensation traced down her spine. "I-I haven't thanked you for what you did today," she said shyly.

"I wasn't as successful as I would have liked. I couldn't get the charges against him dropped, and Gary is not free to leave Greece."

"Still . . . he's out of jail," she murmured.

A sprinkle of stars lit the velvet purple of the darkening sky. When Alexander's hand reached across the table for hers, she did not pull away. All of her wariness was gone. She felt deeply contented—just being with him.

"You seem happier today," he said at last, "as if you're adjusting to your new life—with me."

His broad smile was disarming, and in that moment she believed that her happiness was very important to him. She thought back over the evening. Rarely had she ever been happier. She remembered their swim and their dinner together. The three of them—Gary, Alexander, and herself—had had such lighthearted fun together. It was almost as though they were a real family. It was a feeling she had not experienced since her mother's death. As she stared at the darkly good-looking man opposite her who gazed at her so warmly, she knew she would treasure the memory of this evening forever.

The sunlight glimmering on the aquamarine surface of the pool was no brighter than the spirits of the beautiful girl who observed it. Her cheeks were flushed with a radiance that betrayed her inner joy. Two weeks had passed since Alexander had obtained Gary's release.

Helen sighed blissfully. Surely this was the most

beautiful morning of her life. Above her in a pine tree, a bird trilled a haunting lovesong.

Her fingertips wound around her coffee cup. Before Gary and Alexander had left for work, the three of them had spent a warm, intimate breakfast hour. Dreamily, she touched the tingling place on her forehead where Alexander's lips had brushed her skin with an affectionate good-bye kiss, promising to return for lunch—so that he could spend those hours with her.

The past two weeks had changed everything! Alexander's genuine kindness and interest toward her brother had made her see him in an entirely new light. Alexander had been working diligently to have the charges against Gary dropped.

She had been wrong about him! This fact seemed to sing in her mind. She had been so sure that Alexander was like her father that she hadn't once judged him on his own merit. Just because he was handsome and devastatingly attractive did not mean he was the callous heartbreaker her father was! She had been childish and rash to accuse him of it.

She thought back over their relationship. From the first she had misjudged him. Her distrust had made her see everything he did as being a coldly calculating attempt at seduction. Yet she had spent a great deal of time with him, and she had to admit that he had exercised the utmost restraint.

But if he was not intent on a mere physical relationship with her, what was his motive? Why did he want her with him?

The unanswered question was like music in her heart. When he had first asked her to stay in Greece, he'd said he wanted to see if his attraction for her was based on anything more than physical desire. And now she wondered happily—was it?

A rush of excitement left her breathless. Never had

she felt so exhilarated. She felt she couldn't wait to see Alexander again.

Oh, the day was far too beautiful to spend at the piano! She would take one more day off! She would go to the flower market and purchase the flowers herself that Alexander so loved. She would make the house beautiful—for him. For no reason at all, it seemed terribly important to her to do something, however small, to please him.

One hour later Helen, her arms laden with blossoms as bright as the joy filling her heart, paused in the entranceway of the house to stare in puzzlement at the mountain of expensive leather suitcases stacked near the marble staircase.

An odd little tremor of fear nagged her. *Who . . . ?* The question had no chance to form in Helen's mind before the answer presented herself in person.

Natasha, gowned in flowing white silk and fluffs of ostrich feathers, glided into the salon with the liquid grace of a dark swan. At the sight of Helen, a frown creased her beautiful face.

"Who are you? And what are you doing—here?" the Russian demanded imperiously.

"Why, I-I am Alex's . . . Mr. Marianatos's secretary," Helen faltered. Her hollow voice sounded unnatural. "I-I didn't realize he was expecting guests."

"I haven't seen you before," the older woman said. "You must be a new addition to his staff." She paused. "My dear, I think I should explain I am not just a guest of Alexis. When I am in Athens, I live with him!" Her brilliant eyes flashed with the cold fire of emeralds, and it was impossible to mistake her meaning.

Natasha's softly spoken words were like an unexpected physical blow. Helen emitted a strangled sigh, and the bouquet she was holding spilled to the floor. All the

135

bright gaiety of the morning was spoiled. She wanted to run from the room, from this woman whose offhanded remark had produced the ache of her heart. But pride froze her limbs into immobility and pasted a polite smile on her face. Silently, she stooped to retrieve the flowers.

The only outward sign of her inner suffering was the single tear that traced a path down her cheek and splashed onto the petals of the first red rose she picked up.

Chapter Eight

"If you are Alexis's new secretary, then why have you spent your morning at the flower market instead of at his office?" There was an arrogant demand in the thickly accented, honeyed tones.

A thorn pricked the soft flesh of Helen's palm and she winced. "I . . ."

Before she could answer, Maria appeared. Briefly nodding toward Natasha, she addressed Helen: "Kiria, is Kirie Marianatos coming home for lunch?"

In a voice that sounded much more composed than she felt, Helen responded, "Yes, he is. And I'll come into the kitchen in a minute to help you with the menu." Suddenly anxious to rid herself of the flowers she'd so joyously purchased, Helen stood up and handed them to Maria. "Please arrange these," she began with attempted indifference, "before Alexander . . ."—she flushed at her inadvertent slip; quickly, she corrected herself—". . . Mr. Marianatos arrives."

Helen was very aware of Natasha's cold stare. When Maria left them, the dancer said in a voice that was falsely sweet, "There is no need now for you to answer my question. Maria has supplied the answer. It's obvious you're one of his . . . women."

Anger suffused Helen's cheeks with brightness. "I am not!"

"There's no reason for you to deny the truth . . . to me. I am a cosmopolitan woman. I am not in the least shocked by your relationship with him. In fact, why don't we have Maria bring us a cool drink out on the terrace while we enjoy a cozy little chat?"

Helen expelled a quick breath in shock. Natasha's accusation, followed by her poised acceptance of Helen as Alexander's mistress—even though she wasn't!—was deeply disturbing.

A *cozy little chat* was the last thing Helen wanted, but she could think of no way to elude Natasha.

A pale blue sofa and matching chairs were nestled beneath the shady veranda outside the grand salon overlooking the terraces. Warily settling amidst the plump cushions, Helen regarded Natasha. The black-haired dancer was as startlingly beautiful as Helen remembered. Her slightest gesture was one of flawless grace.

Helen's dry throat constricted. How could she have thought—even for a moment—that Alexander had been serious about her, when he could have such a stunning woman?

"You are probably surprised that I can accept you so readily," Natasha began magnanimously. "But then . . . if you knew Alexis . . . as I do . . . you would realize that such relationships are his norm."

Helen's stomach twisted painfully. So . . . Alexander . . . and Natasha . . . He *was* exactly like her father! She had foolishly let herself be duped by his kindnesses to Gary and his seemingly sincere warmth toward herself. She felt almost faint—as though she had suffered a deep, internal wound.

The honeyed voice continued, sickeningly sweet. "I would not want to see you hurt, my dear. Enjoy him, but take care not to become too involved with him. He may seem fond of you now, but you'll marvel how quickly he'll come to despise you—once he tires of you in his bed."

Natasha's face swam in nauseating circles. "I-I'm not sharing his bed," Helen choked.

"How strange. I was under the impression that you were living here . . . with him."

"I do live here . . . but not with him in the way you're implying."

"But . . . how is that possible? Alexis is not the kind of man to be long amused holding hands with a woman he wants."

"Alexander and I are friends."

"Pillow friends." Natasha's quick laughter was brittle, and it cut to Helen's heart like a sharp blade.

How could this woman think . . . but, then, why shouldn't she? Natasha knew him so well; obviously, she entertained no girlish illusions about the kind of man he was. Helen's heartbreak changed suddenly to blind, jealous fury. Her carefully polite words were cooly clipped when she spoke: "You deliberately misunderstand me!"

"I? Misunderstand?" Natasha's silky voice disbelieved. "That dress you are wearing—he selected it from Madame Moreau's shop, didn't he?" Helen could only nod mutely. "You see how well I know my Alexis and his tastes in clothes? You may be assured I know him just as well in other areas. He is not the type of man who dresses a woman to his tastes, invites her to share his home, and does not take her to his bed."

Emerald-green, cat-like eyes observed Helen's swift intake of breath with cold satisfaction.

"It is not like that between us! It isn't! My brother was in trouble, and Alexander . . ."

"Tut-tut." Natasha waved her hands theatrically. "You can save your explanations for others who may have the patience to listen. It is obvious that this is your first affair, and you still find it a little embarrassing. Well, we will talk no more of it. I have no wish to make you more uncomfortable with your 'position' than you already are. You and I, we will have to get along, for if you're living with Alexis, we will be seeing a great deal of one another."

Although her words were kind, her manner was not. Helen sensed a fierce hostility lurking just beneath the surface of the suavely beautiful dancer.

There seemed to be nothing more to say, and the two women lapsed into an uncomfortable silence. Helen sat with her eyes downcast; the rest of her features remained rigidly immobile, for she had no wish to betray her pain. She was on the verge of excusing herself to go to the kitchen when she caught sight of Alexander, home earlier than she'd anticipated, striding masterfully across the veranda toward them.

A mad tempo pounded against her eardrums. How could she face him after what Natasha had just said?

He was whistling a jaunty tune she'd heard once in a *taverna*. His dark face was animated with joy. For an instant Helen's own heart lightened at the sight of him before another unhappy realization struck her. Doubtless he'd come home early to be with Natasha.

When his lips brushed her own cheek lightly in greeting, a searing pain sliced through Helen. The kiss was no more than a routine gesture to him; it meant nothing. Natasha was the woman he desired.

Alexander's arms around her stiffened as he saw Natasha—as if for the first time—snugly settled against the deep pillows in the shadows. "Natasha, what are you doing here?"

Helen detected no warmth in his low, melodious voice.

"Had you forgotten that I was coming?" Natasha queried sweetly, looking up at him through her thick, fan-like black lashes. "Darling, for a financier, you are terribly absentminded. But then you have a new distraction. . . ." As she eyed Helen's stiffly erect form, Alexander's arms dropped away. "I have just met your *latest* . . . little . . . er . . . friend." She had already forgotten Helen's name.

"Helen," he supplied in a deep, irritated tone. His voice grew even firmer. "Natasha, what are you doing in Athens?"

Helen's mind was racing to interpret the situation. He did not seem overjoyed to see Natasha, but that was probably only because he was feeling guilty that she had caught him with another woman.

"Don't you remember that you offered to loan me your villa again to rehearse *The Firebird* before my company performs in the Athens Festival of Music and Drama to honor you, Greece's own bird of fire. I accepted the invitation only to please you . . . to honor you for all you have done for me." She rose, her silk gown flowing around her graceful movements, and encircled him with her arms. Her lips closed over his so possessively that Helen could not doubt the depth of Natasha's feelings for him.

Gently, Alexander disengaged her. "I thought I made it clear I didn't want any more publicity about our friendship," he said. "And you told me in Paris you hadn't been invited to perform in the festival."

"Darling, that was true then, but I have now. There were certain difficulties," she said vaguely, dismissing the fiery battle she'd waged with a charming, fluttery wave of her hand. "*The Firebird* is not classical Greek drama, for one thing. Still, the obstacles were not insurmountable."

"Not for you, Natasha," Alexander murmured, the trace of a smile curving his hard mouth for the first time.

Natasha rushed on. "I've already booked hotel rooms for the other performers. Tomorrow the sets will arrive. Of course, I won't be able to use most of them because of the design of the Odeon of Herodos Atticus." Helen remembered the ancient Roman theater from her tour and could imagine the difficulties in performing a ballet there. "Darling, you do remember you promised me at my party that I could store the sets here and rehearse in your theater . . . if I were invited."

"Only vaguely. It never occurred to me there was the slightest possibility you would be invited."

"Well, I have been." Natasha's smile of triumph was bright. She took his acquiescence that she could use his theater for granted. After a brief pause, she said, "The party you gave me *was* wonderful. I am wishing we could have another . . . here . . . soon . . . before the performance." When he only stared grimly down at her, Natasha asked, "Alexis, couldn't we?"

"I really have a very tight schedule right now, Natasha." Tightly leashed impatience edged his voice.

"Please," she begged, allowing her bristly black lashes to flutter with coy artifice.

Alexander turned toward Helen. As his dark gaze, growing undeniably warm and intimate, fell upon her, his firm, unyielding expression softened. Every nerve in Helen's body quivered in response. She had felt very much the outsider listening to him talk to Natasha, but now—when he looked at her like that . . . Mentally, she pushed back the tide of happiness that threatened to wash away her good sense, and she returned his friendly look with a frigid one of her own.

"Well," he began, "I suppose it would be the perfect opportunity for me to introduce Helen to my friends. All right, Natasha, you can have your party."

Even though Alexander had given in to her demand, Natasha was not entirely satisfied. Her beautiful face remained petulant.

"Do you really think introducing Helen to your friends would be the proper thing?" she asked silkily.

Embarrassment scalded Helen's cheeks with brightness. She had done nothing wrong! But everyone would think . . .

By forcing her to live with him, Alexander had placed her in a most untenable position. Helen couldn't bear to hear more. They were discussing her as if she were not present! Without excusing herself, she ran blindly, stumbling from the veranda. She ignored Alexander when he called after her. Once outside the mansion, she paused to catch her breath. Her heart was pounding painfully.

She heard their voices clearly as they drifted through the opened doors of the grand salon.

"Natasha, when did you ever give a whit for propriety?"

"I mean, do you think she'll fit in with . . . our crowd?" Her lovely voice was condescending.

"Of course she'll fit in!" Alexander snapped, coldly furious.

"Don't be angry, darling. I was only thinking of her."

143

Helen swallowed and brushed back the tears that were threatening to fall.

Natasha's presence in Alexander's house, as well as the things she had said, hurt far more deeply than they should.

Now she knew for sure Alexander was exactly the kind of man she had first assumed he was: worldly, sophisticated, jaded. His kindnesses were insincere. His feelings for her were base and shallow. And yet . . . She pushed away the memory of the past two glorious weeks.

She drew a deep, shaky breath to calm herself. Slowly, she turned toward her room.

When she reached her suite, she locked herself inside. Her heart thumped desperately, and tears, unchecked, flowed down her cheeks.

A quarter of an hour later a soft knock shattered the silence in her bedroom. Ignoring the sound, she buried her head deeply into her pillow. The knock—now brisk and loud—persisted.

"Helen, quit acting like a child and open the door. I want to talk to you."

It was Alexander! He must never, never know the reason for her tears! Her pride would at least remain intact, if not her heart.

"Go away!" she called out desperately. "I don't want to talk to you—ever!"

"You will talk to me—and now!"

Rebellion burst through her at the authoritarian ring in his deep voice, but she realized the futility of further defiance. She knew he would break the door down if he had to.

"All right. . . ." Slowly, she dragged herself from the bed and smoothed her hair back from her tear-stained face.

When she opened the door, Alexander strode inside. His raven-black hair was disheveled, his expression grim. The feminine bedroom contrasted sharply with his overpowering virility, making Helen even more aware of it.

His penetrating black gaze swept over her. "Why . . . you've been crying," he said, his deep voice oddly gentle.

"Yes, I have!" she answered shrilly, attempting to cover her own vulnerability where he was concerned with anger. "I suppose you've come here to gloat."

"Gloat! Is that what you think?" he rasped, barely holding his temper in check.

She nodded.

"For your information, I came to apologize about Natasha," he muttered through clenched jaws. "But, as usual, you attribute the worst of motives to me."

Everything Natasha had said came back with sweeping force. "And I'm right in doing so," she accused.

"What is that supposed to mean?"

"Oh, what's the use?" she pleaded. "Why won't you just let me go? Let me leave Greece."

"Have you forgotten Gary and the charges against him?"

"No, I haven't," she murmured in quiet defeat.

There was a troubled glint in his jet-dark eyes; the expression on his darkly handsome face was one of true concern. Why couldn't he be the man he seemed? His mere presence was torture to her.

"Why won't you just go away and leave me alone?" she whispered.

"I will—once we get to the bottom of this." He reached for her, and although his touch was gentle, she sprang away as though she'd felt fire.

"Don't touch me!"

"All right," he replied reasonably. "But I want to know what I've done now. Why are you so angry?"

"Am I really the first woman who's seen you for the man you really are?" she hedged, hoping to divert him.

"You're certainly the first who's tried my patience to the limits of its endurance." Anger vibrated in his tightly controlled voice.

"Alexander Marianatos, your ego can't endure a woman who doesn't swoon every time you look at her, a woman who sees you exactly as you are."

He drew in a deep, calming breath; his patience returned. "If my motives are so reprehensible, what about your own?" he taunted, turning the tables on her.

"My motives?"

"Yes—yours, my self-righteous little one." The faintest smile curved his hard lips. "Perhaps the reason you are so suspicious of me all the time is because you operate from questionable motives yourself."

"I . . . T-that's ridiculous!"

"I don't think so." He was no longer angry himself, and a devilish, mocking light snapped in his dark eyes. "Why did you come to me in the first place—if not to use me?"

"You know that's not why I came! I wanted you to help my brother!"

"That's only your interpretation! I could interpret the situation differently. You wanted to use me for your own gain!"

She inhaled a deep, indignant breath, sputtering. "W-why, you would think of something like that! When it was you who decided to use my brother and what you could do for him to keep me here—to suit your own vile purposes!"

" 'Vile'—that's a very ugly word," he scolded gently. A slow smile softened his grim expression. "I don't like your applying it to me and my conduct toward you when you've been treated as an honored guest in my house."

"You know as well as I do that I'm no ordinary guest," she countered stiffly, trying to ignore the persuasive charm of his smile.

"So we're back to that, are we?" One black brow arched jeeringly. "Ah, yes. . . . I have you here—to seduce you." His sensually knowing gaze roving over her curves caused a tremor of uneasiness to flow through her limbs. "I can't help being curious as to how you can explain why I haven't done so." Swiftly, he was beside her. Deftly, his brown fingers caught the yellow silk scarf she'd casually looped around her neck, and slowly, in a deliberately sensuous manner, he pulled it.

The loose knot yielded, and the soft fabric sliding against the smooth flesh of her throat caused her pulse to race. The hushed silence between them grew electric.

Carelessly, he tossed the scarf to the bed. When he brought his hand back to caress the exposed flesh of her shoulder, the sensations his touch aroused were so pleasant she did nothing to stop him. He pushed down the narrow strap of her sundress. His fingers traced a tingling path across the warm flesh swelling gently above the lacy bodice of her yellow sundress. Relentlessly, he held her gaze, saying, "It's hardly because we've lacked the opportunity."

His words broke the spell, shocking her back to reality.

"Why, you . . . how can you be so insolent?" she gasped.

"Not insolent—truthful." He removed his hand. Dry

147

amusement quirked the corners of his mouth. "I was saying, we've had ample opportunity. . . . And, as procrastination is not one of my bad habits, wouldn't I have seduced you long ago, if that were my intention?" His black eyes pierced into her, mocking her. Suddenly, a tightness gripped her throat. "Do I need to remind you that I could have easily accomplished that on our first date? Indeed—I could easily accomplish it now."

His knowledgeable eyes flicked quickly past her to the vast bed, where the discarded bright silk ripple hinted he could just as easily have removed the rest of her clothes.

His arrogant recollection of their first date, as well his present assumption that he could seduce her now, caused her cheeks to burn as though she had a fever. Angrily, she pulled up the strap of her dress and moved away from him.

"You would bring that night up and . . . insinuate . . ." She broke off, flustered.

"Only to prove to you that I'm telling the truth," he said, negligently shrugging his shoulders. "I've never had the slightest intention of seducing you. Hasn't it occurred to you that in this age of easy morality I could find any number of women who would be happy to move in with me *if* that was what I wanted? I have no need to keep you here for that purpose."

Strangely enough, what he said made sense. Suddenly, Helen felt herself a naïve fool.

"Alexander, I-I do believe you," she said tremulously.

"It's about time," was his crisp retort.

"But . . . Alexander . . . there's one thing . . . I don't know. Why did you insist I stay in Greece?"

"I think you know the answer to that." His low voice was warm.

Heartbeats pounded her chest in an excited rush. Could it be . . . ? Was he . . . ? The question was so intoxicating she pushed it from her mind.

Quietly he began, chosing his words carefully. "I wanted to help you. Is it so difficult to believe that I was operating from the same motive as yourself? You wanted to help your brother; I wanted to help you. You were a lovely young woman, yet you were burying yourself in your music. You would have left Greece . . . and me . . . and continued to run away from yourself. Work isn't all there is to life, Helen. I didn't want you to go before you learned how to enjoy just being alive."

"How very Greek you are," she said softly, hoping she didn't reveal how acutely disappointed she was by his answer. She had thought he would say—she had hoped he would say—that he loved her.

"You never did tell me why you were crying," he murmured gently.

"I-I . . ." His question took her completely by surprise. All of the terrible things Natasha had said about him came flooding back.

"Was it Natasha?"

"Yes . . . in a way."

"I wasn't expecting her. If I'd known she was coming, I would have asked her not to."

"You d-don't want her here?" There was a curious, breathless quality in her light voice.

"No. Not now." His mouth quirked as he gazed tenderly down at her, causing her heart to skip a beat. "Natasha has a way of taking over—everything. You see, she's a star and terribly spoiled. She's a very difficult woman to live with."

Helen realized with a pang he was speaking from experience. What, *exactly*, was his relationship with the dancer? And what sort of relationships did he have with other woman? Those were questions she didn't dare to ask.

That night Alexander found Helen in the garden.

"Helen . . ."

His deep voice vibrated through her. She turned quickly, a look of startled expectancy illuminating her beautiful face. Her hair gleamed in the moonlight; her silvery gown shimmered.

"Yes . . . Alexander."

He loomed beside her, suavely elegant in his evening clothes. "Natasha was a bit much tonight, wasn't she?" he began. "I hope she didn't upset you."

"No," Helen lied. All evening Natasha had monopolized Alexander, telling private jokes and deliberately speaking Greek whenever possible to exclude Helen. The dancer, exquisite in low-cut scarlet chiffon, had done everything in her power to make Helen feel ill at ease.

"Natasha told me you'd offered to play *The Firebird Suite* for her during rehearsals until her own pianist recovers from the flu. Did she coerce you into that?" Alexander's alert gaze studied her carefully.

"No. I made the offer myself."

Some of the tension eased from his lean features. "Well, that's a relief. I won't have her bullying you." A protective note had crept into his deep voice. In a less serious vein, he said, "If anyone's going to boss or bully you—it's going to be me," he teased, grinning down at her.

She knew he was making light of her previous accusations, and her sense of humor surfaced. She could not wholly suppress the beginnings of the smile twitching her lips. "I can't make up my mind who's bossier—you or Natasha."

"Definitely Natasha!" he exclaimed, his grin broadening. "But enough of her! I came out here to see you."

Helen was glad suddenly of the darkness, for it concealed her face. She was sure the heady sensations his words had produced would otherwise have been clearly revealed.

His hand closed tightly over hers, and he drew her more deeply into the garden.

Helen sighed. If only Natasha hadn't come, it would have been a sigh of utter contentment. But Natasha had come, and it was impossible to forget everything she'd said. Nor could Helen forget how miserably left out she herself had felt during and after dinner, while Natasha had claimed Alexander's undivided attention.

Helen had observed them together closely: both so dark and vibrant; two strong-willed international personalities. They were two of a kind. They belonged together.

Helen tried to swallow the dry ache in her throat. Doubtless Alexander had only sought her out in the garden because he felt sorry for her.

She tugged against her hand so firmly held in his, withdrawing it.

"Did you come out here for any special reason?" she asked, forcing her voice to sound nonchalant.

"Ah, yes," he mocked. She felt his sharp, amused glance. "You are the girl who believes I always have an ulterior motive."

"Alexander, don't tease me."

"Why not? You deserve it." His black eyes sparkled mischievously. "Suppose I confessed that you were right all along." He flashed her a wicked smile. "Suppose I am a true Lothario, who's lured you to the farthest edge of his garden to make love to you. How would you defend yourself?"

151

Her heart was an excited drumbeat against her chest. Every nerve in her body was aware of Alexander's towering, male presence. "Why, I-I would run back to the . . ." Cautiously, she was backing away from him.

"Oh, no, you wouldn't." His strong arm circled her waist possessively, his expression gravely serious as he gazed intently into her eyes.

"Alexander! Don't play with me!"

He held her to him with effortless ease. "I'm not playing with you, Helen. I do want to make love to you."

His dark head bent to her bright one; his hard mouth closed over her soft lips. Helen lifted her hands as if to push him away, but instead they circled his neck, increasing the pressure of his mouth against her own.

Her head spun dizzily because of his ardent caresses, and she felt her resistance weakening, yielding beneath the assault of his kisses.

His fierce passion awoke yearnings she'd sought to suppress. She was reminded of all the lonely nights when she'd slept alone, of future nights that would be all the more lonely because she wanted him. *She loved him.* She accepted this realization because it was impossible for her to deny it any longer.

She loved him! And if he'd returned her love, she would have gladly given herself to him, but she knew she was just another conquest to him.

His voice murmuring against her ear was hoarse and indistinct—yet urgent in its demand. His fingers combed the flaming tresses that tumbled to her shoulders. As always, his lovemaking was expert.

How many other women had there been? And how was she any different from the rest?

Gently, she pushed against the broad expanse of his muscular chest, and he released her.

"What's the matter?" he asked, frowning.

"I-I can't," she managed in a ragged whisper.

"I never expected you to. Not here, darling."

His words implied that she would elsewhere. "I want to go inside," she said shakily.

"In a minute. Helen, I've told you before you have no reason to be afraid of me. I'm not going to force you to do anything you don't want to—ever. But sometimes when I hold you—I want to go on holding you and kissing you . . . and . . ."

"I know. . . ." She was beginning to wonder how much longer she would be able to deny what they both longed to experience. "Alexander, I really do think we should go. . . ."

"All right."

Together they walked down the garden path toward the house. When they reached the sculptured hedge bordering the terraces, he said, "I did come out to the garden for a reason."

"Oh . . ."

"I wanted to ask a favor of you. I know you'll be busy with Natasha's rehearsals, but could you help me plan that party she wants? I may be busier than usual at the office for the next week or two."

So—he'd come to find her because of Natasha. Helen felt unreasonably crushed. Quietly, she said, "I would be glad to, Alexander. But Natasha . . . won't she object?"

"I don't think so. She's used to having others carry out her grand plans."

Together they walked down the garden path toward the house.

Uneasily, Helen remembered Natasha's remarks about his women. Would loving him ever mean she would become as sophisticated as Natasha and accept the other women in his life? She couldn't imagine it.

Chapter Nine

Her tightly fitting black satin gown rustling, Helen moved gracefully across her bedroom to stand before the long windows that looked out onto the grounds. Some of the guests had already arrived, and at the sight of them—so glamorous—she felt coldly fearful. She couldn't help wondering if Natasha had been right about her own inability to fit in with these people. Nervously, Helen fingered the flashing diamond necklace Alexander had given her and insisted she wear tonight. Then her thoughts returned to the dancer.

Natasha! She was omnipresent! She had taken over everything—Alexander, his home, Gary, and even herself. When Helen hadn't been playing the piano for her rehearsals, she'd been occupied with planning this party. There'd been the caterers, the florists, the musicians, and the servants to organize; and Natasha's constant additions to the guest list. . . . Helen was exhausted.

Alexander had been away frequently, yet somehow, in spite of Natasha's constant interferences when he was home, he'd found the time to spark an interest in

Gary for mechanical engineering. For the first time her brother was speaking about college with enthusiasm.

As she thought of the two of them, Helen smiled gently. Alexander—so regally self-possessed; her brother—so filled with admiration for the older man. If only Hal had shown Gary half the understanding Alexander had, many of the boy's problems might have been avoided.

Glancing apprehensively down at her glittering wristwatch, she realized she couldn't put off going down any longer. She glided softly across the room and out onto the landing overlooking the grand salon. One dainty sparkling evening slipper peeped from beneath the slit of her daring satin gown as she hesitantly placed her foot on the first step of the winding staircase.

Natasha's bright laughter floating from the salon caused Helen to pause at the top of the stairs. The dancer, gowned in a sequined blouse with a flowing, emerald-green skirt, stood beside Alexander. Together they greeted their guests. A French film star and her entourage had just arrived, and Natasha was gushing effusively.

Suddenly, Alexander, as though restless, glanced upward and saw Helen. His dark gaze swept over her. Excusing himself, he moved toward her with his easy grace, taking the steps two at a time.

Natasha's vivacious laughter ceased, and the dancer, her beautiful lips freezing in an artificial smile, stared coldly up at Helen.

Helen flushed hotly. Alexander's rash behavior had called obvious attention to her presence. Everyone was staring up at them. Never had she felt more ill at ease!

It was the dress! she thought wildly. Why had Alexander insisted she wear this bodly revealing gown? It was much too sophisticated for her. It's plunging V neckline, the soft fabric molding her curving figure, left far too little to the imagination. And every time she took a step, her long, shapely legs were exposed by the slashed skirt.

Alexander, resplendent in his ink-black tux and ruffled dress shirt, had reached her and was smiling warmly down at her. She stared up at him anxiously. He took her trembling hand in his and folded it across his arm.

"I-I can't go down," she whispered, clinging to the railing. "Those people are famous. They won't want to meet me."

"Nonsense." Slowly, he led her downward.

"Alexander, everyone's looking at me! It's this dress! They find it shocking!"

"It's not the dress, but your beauty, my little one, that shocks them." His dark eyes glowed with pride.

"Flattery will get you nowhere. I know it's the dress. I feel almost naked in it!"

"I've seen you in less!" he teased.

"What? I'd like to know when!" she exclaimed, so provoked she forgot her nervousness.

"Well—that lavender bikini you sometimes wear when you sun on your deck is quite . . . er . . . tantalizing."

"Alexander!" She had never given a thought to the fact that the loft overlooked her balcony. "How could you spy on me?"

"How could any normal man resist?"

He was smiling warmly down at her, and suddenly it was a struggle to suppress an answering smile of her own. Still, she would have issued a stinging retort to set him properly in his place had they not reached the bottom of the stairs, where they were immediately surrounded by his guests.

All were anxious to meet the stunning young woman on their host's arm. They greeted her so warmly that she soon forgot her nervousness. When a Norwegian prince with a serious interest in classical music claimed her attention, Alexander left her so that he could mingle with his guests.

Time passed, and Alexander did not return. Helen had last seen him, a beautiful woman tucked on either arm, as he headed down the hall that led to his collection of antiquities. How well she remembered that first night when she'd been the girl he'd led down that hall.

She remembered Natasha's insinuations—that Alexander was a man who liked many women. Suddenly, in spite of the fact that she was surrounded by people, Helen felt very lonely and forlorn. Rationally, she knew that he was a host, and as such he must attend to his guests—be they men or women.

Still, his inattentiveness hurt, and she could take no satisfaction in the obvious success of the party. The orchestra played soft, melodious music. Silver trays overflowed with tempting hors d'oeuvres: *champignons à la montebello,* avocado crabmeat rampart, shrimp de jonghe, *escargots bourguignonne.*

There was much laughter and gaiety. Yet Helen felt strangely alienated from the others. She drifted through the crowded rooms alone. With the unerring cunning of a shark sensing a vulnerable victim, Natasha came to her.

"Everyone is having a wonderful time tonight," she said, pausing to emphasize what she said next. "Especially . . . Alexis." She stared past Helen toward the hall where he had disappeared so long ago. "He does enjoy beautiful young things so. . . . And they enjoy him. Of course . . . you know that, having felt the impact yourself of his . . . admiration." Her sharp green gaze studied Helen carefully, calculating the effect of her words.

When Helen paled visibly, Natasha smiled wickedly, admonishing, "If you are wise, you will accept him as he is. Amuse yourself with another man while he dallies."

A man called to Natasha, and laughing, she glided away—doubtless, heeding her own advice.

Helen's chin lifted as she successfully fought back the tears that wanted to fall. She had to get away! Away from Alexander! And his friends! Their sophistication was inhuman! She was herself incapable of using a man for diversion because the man she loved philandered. She was totally out of her element.

Just as she was about to make her escape, a man, who'd been watching Natasha and her, gently caught her arm. He was older, distinguished, and obviously Greek. His luminous dark eyes were sympathetic.

"Miss Freeman, you are Gary's sister, I believe?" he questioned softly.

"Yes."

"I am Mr. Megas, the official responsible for the grave error concerning your brother."

"Oh . . ."

"I was out of the country at the time of your brother's arrest," Mr. Megas confessed. "And one of my subordinates overreacted to the situation. I am very, very sorry."

"That's all right . . . now. Gary and I were terrified when it happened. No one would believe anything we said."

"I'm sure it was terrible for you both, but you were lucky to have the support of Alexander. When he came to me and told me your brother was innocent, I arranged for his release at once."

"Why did Alexander's intercession make any difference?" she asked, wondering if he owed Alexander a political favor.

"Because Alexander is a man of impeccable character. He has never asked me for any favors for himself. He is the kind of man who would never try to free a criminal no matter what his connection to him. He had looked into your brother's case very carefully, and he quickly convinced me of his innocence."

"I'm deeply grateful to Alexander for helping Gary," she murmured.

"Indeed, all of Greece is grateful to him," Mr. Megas continued. "In spite of his fabulous wealth, he never forgets those less fortunate than himself. He is one of Greece's foremost philanthropists. Only the other day he donated an enormous sum of money to fund a new hospital for burn victims."

"He did?" She could scarcely digest this unexpected piece of information. Once she had rashly accused him of being ruthless.

Mr. Megas would have eagerly told her more, had not one of the maids interrupted them.

"Kiria, there is a man in the library who wishes to see you."

"Why didn't you bring him to me?"

"He is not an invited guest, Kiria. He insists that you see him . . . alone."

Graciously, Helen excused herself and walked quickly to the library. When she opened the library doors, a familiar sandy head peered up from a book, jolting her.

What was Bill Simpson doing here? Tonight?

"Bill . . ." His name was a sound strangling in her throat. Involuntarily, her hand went to her neck to conceal the flashing diamonds. She longed for a wrap to cover herself properly . . . anything!

His deep blue eyes swept over her, widening as he

noted the provocative curve of her breasts above the low-cut gown, her narrow waist encased in tight satin, and the wanton exposure of shapely legs revealed by her daring skirt.

His gentle expression changed to one of puzzled shock. He said in a voice that was deceptively mild, "That's some dress!"

If only dear, unsophisticated Bill hadn't seen her like this! As she hurried across the room to greet him, she flushed so deeply her complexion was nearly as bright as her hair.

To her surprise, he took the hand she extended to him and used it to pull her into his arms. He amazed her still more by holding her tightly to him for a very long time, as though she were much more to him than a friend. Gallantly, he made no further comments about how she had changed.

"Helen, it's wonderful to see you."

"I'm glad to see you too, Bill," she managed to say.

"If I'd realized you were having a party, I wouldn't have come by 'til the morning. I'm hardly dressed. . . ."

"You know you're always welcome in my home."

"Do you consider this your home now?" he asked, his usually gentle voice unnaturally hard.

"I . . . I do live here."

"I came as quickly as I could get away," he said. "You sounded pretty upset on the phone—when you told me to cancel your tour. Hal gave me your address."

"Oh, Bill, I was . . . upset . . . then. But you shouldn't have come—not all this way! Alexander has taken care of everything. Gary's free now—out of prison on bail. I think the charges against him will be dropped very shortly." Her delicate brows knitted into a frown. "Oh, I should have realized you'd worry.

Why didn't I call and let you know that we were all right?"

"Alexander—is he the man who owns this house?" Bill asked with studied directness as his eyes zeroed in on the collar of diamonds circling her neck.

"Y-yes."

Bill's serious expression was one of silent disapproval. His eyes did not leave the necklace. Quietly, he said, "Helen, this is not the kind of life for you. What are you—his kept woman?"

A pulsebeat pounded furiously against her temple. "No! Bill! You must believe me!"

He responded reassuringly as an adult would to soothe a child. "Of course I believe you. But don't you see where living with him has to lead?" She could think of nothing to say. "I'm glad I refused to cancel your contract. I want you to pack immedaitely. I'll book you on a flight to New York."

Unable to meet his eyes, she shifted her weight from one foot to the other. "Oh, Bill, if only it were that simple."

So engrossed were they in their conversation that the faint sound from the doorway did not distract them.

"Of course it's that simple," he insisted.

"I . . . I can't come."

"Why not? Has this man got some sort of hold on you?" The question was the only sound in the hushed stillness of the library.

When she hesitated for a long moment, the deep, resonant voice of Alexander vibrated through her, shocking her with its command. "Well, answer that question, Helen." She whirled to meet glittering dark eyes in his too-still, hard face. He stood negligently in the frame of the massive doorway. "Have I?"

His presence totally disrupted her senses. "No," she admitted softly at last.

"Why *are* you living with me?" When she said nothing, he demanded harshly, "Tell him!"

"Because . . . I . . . want to."

Bill's large blue eyes on her face wore the expression of a betrayed animal's. "Is that the truth?" he asked, thinking the worst.

"I've told you the truth, Bill. I . . . I want to stay here."

"How you've changed, Helen." His condemning gaze brought new color to her cheeks.

Then she turned from him—her embarrassment acute—and would have run from the room, had not Alexander swiftly seized her. She felt the hard, muscular strength of his arms circling her as he guided her back into the library. Strangely, it was comforting to cling to him for support.

Because she was so upset, Helen failed to notice that Alexander saw very clearly. Bill's look of condemnation was gone, and in its place, as he observed Helen in Alexander's possessive embrace, turbulent feelings mingled: profound anguish, unrequited love, and jealousy.

"You've no need to worry yourself further on Helen's account, Mr. Simpson," Alexander said in a voice that was oddly gentle. "My relationship with her has always been honorable; in fact, next week . . . *she and I are going to be married.*"

Helen was scarcely aware of Bill—his face stricken as though he'd received a staggering blow, his mumble of congratulations, his swift departure. She was still in a state of shock when Alexander spoke to her.

"I halfway thought you'd contradict me." His low voice was husky with emotion.

"What would have been the point," she began shakily, "when we both know, that because of Gary, I'm totally in your power . . . ?"

"I don't think that was your reason at all," he said with alarming perception. "I think living with me in this impossible situation is affecting you in the same way it is affecting me—and you *want* to marry me."

She was shaken to the core by his arrogant statement. Had she been that obvious? Had he seen that she loved him? "That's absurd," she declared with a vehemence she did not feel. She swallowed hard, aware of a strange, yet ecstatic, tension pulsating through her.

He was staring down at her, a challenging, fervent gleam lighting his black eyes. Slowly, he drew her into his arms. Then his mouth was on hers. For several agonizing moments she resisted his kiss. But as his mouth moved upon hers with ardent determination, involuntarily she allowed her lips to part so that his tongue could slide inside against the sweet moistness of her own. He tasted faintly, pleasantly, of brandy.

And as always when he kissed her—when he held her so closely, the contours of her body were shaped to his—she wanted him. Only this time the aching, melting flame of passionate desire enveloping her was even more exquisitely intense.

He was trembling now, and so was she. Her fingers fumbled with the fastenings of his ruffled dress shirt so that she could caress the warm, hard flesh of his tanned torso beneath. Burying his lips in the tumbling masses of her flame-gold hair, he crushed her to him with a passionate groan. Slowly, he drew her down onto the couch.

His experienced fingers parted the zipper at the back of her black satin dress, and the dress slid from her shoulders. For a long moment he looked down at her, at her rosily flushed face, at her gently rounded curves, glowing in the soft golden light of the library. His hands touched her breasts, cupped them. He brushed his roughened fingertips lightly across her tautly erect nipples before his lips descended to taste their honey sweetness. And when he did so, a tiny moan of rapturous delight escaped her lips.

His hands moved slowly over her before he pressed her once more to him. The prickly black hairs of his chest tickled the sensitive flesh of her breasts. He shifted his body so that he covered hers. She felt the iron-hard pressure of his thighs, his rising desire. And an ecstatic shudder shook her as despearte yearning shivered through her.

It seemed to her that no matter how tightly he embraced her, it wasn't tightly enough. Her fingers wound around the nape of his neck, tangling in his ebony-black hair. She wanted to belong to him—completely. Her heart seemed caught in her throat. She loved him—so much.

"Alexander, don't ever . . . ever let me go," she pleaded. Tears dampened her eyelashes as she pressed her soft, full lips against the warmth of his throat.

At the sound of her voice, his body tensed before he suddenly pulled away from her. Vaguely, she was aware of him pushing her dress over her body to cover her, of him pulling the edges of his shirt together. His breathing was still erratic when he swept back the rakish lock of dark hair that had fallen across his brow and pushed Helen gently aside. Abruptly, he rose and strode quickly across the library and locked the doors.

"Alexander, w-what's wrong?" Helen sat up, feeling lost and dazed.

"Give me a minute to get myself together," he said raggedly. "And for God's sake, put your clothes back on."

His brutal words tinged her cheeks with shame. Quickly, she obeyed him.

"I behaved like an animal—like the man you've so often accused me of being," he said with savage self-derision. "Do you realize the library doors were unlocked? Anyone could have come in and found me taking you like any common . . ."

She went to him. Tremulously, she touched his hand with hers. "It wasn't like that, Alexander," she said softly. "I wanted you as much as you wanted me. And I was wrong about the kind of man you are. I should never have accused you of those things."

A slow, lopsided smile crooked his mouth as he gazed tenderly down at her. His black eyes gleamed with their normal boldness. "Perhaps—now—you'll agree that it's not so absurd—our marrying?"

"Yes, Alexander," she admitted breathlessly, "I agree. It's not so absurd—our marrying."

"And will you marry me?"

"The sooner the better," she said softly, hoping her eagerness wasn't too obvious.

"My sentiments exactly," he agreed with arrogant satisfaction. With effortless ease he swept her into his arms and kissed her reverently on the lips. Then lest his physical need for her betray him, he quickly released her.

It was only later that she realized that although he had asked her to marry him and he had demonstrated his physical desire for her, not once had he spoken of love.

Chapter Ten

Pulling the filmy folds of her peignoir together, Helen took a quick, deep breath of fresh sea air. The view from her balcony was spectacular. Early morning haze softened the jagged edges of barren rock plunging a sheer thousand feet to the glassy Aegean beneath. She could just see Alexander's yacht moored atop a perfect reflection of itself.

Below her, a gray tabby yawned and stretched lazily on the whitewashed doorstep of a Byzantine chapel. White cube houses zigzagged down a narrow lane toward the deep, blue circle of water.

The quaint charm of the Isle of Marianatos had enchanted Helen the moment she'd stepped from the gangplank of Alexander's yacht. His family had received her very warmly, as though their son's sudden and unexpected marriage, even to a foreigner, was a dream come true; Alexander himself had been attentively adoring. And this morning—her wedding day promised to be a beautiful one.

The wedding ceremony, solemnly performed in an ancient cliffside chapel, with sunlight filtering through jewel-dark stained-glass windows, had been as beautiful as the day. Gary had flown in by helicopter from Athens so that he could give his sister away. Hal, of course, had been too busy to attend.

The boisterous festivities afterward stretched late into the night. The brightly costumed men and women separated according to their sex—frequently mingling to dance together. Alexander had joined his father and a group of men on the far side of the room. There was much wine, music, and revelry as the islanders celebrated their master's marriage.

Very few of the women spoke English well enough to converse with Helen. Mainly, they could only nod and smile at her, so that in spite of their friendliness, she felt left out. A party was going on, but she could not participate. She longed for the time when Alexander would come and they could be alone together.

She heard a burst of deep laughter, and peering through the midst of well-wishers thronging around her, Helen caught a glimpse of Alexander, his black head thrown back, his shirtsleeves rolled halfway up his brown arms. He was part of a swaying circle dancing Greek-style to folk music. Beside him was a beautiful young girl.

Helen swallowed against the aching tightness of her throat, and she tried to smile brightly at the nearest woman, who was beaming at her. Then suddenly from behind her, protective arms gently circled her waist.

"Andrea . . ." Helen murmured gratefully. At least Alexander's younger sister spoke beautiful English.

"You look tired, Helen. Why don't we steal away for a little while. This will go on all night. It is a custom of our island." Andrea's darkly glowing eyes were sympathetic. "It's never easy to be around strangers . . . and Alexander . . . he cannot ignore his old friends, even though this is his wedding day," she said, leading

167

Helen outside toward the terraces sloping down to the cliffs.

A solitary windmill was a miniature pepperpot against a violet sky. For a while the two women walked in silence.

"Alexander is having the time of his life tonight—he is so happy—because of you," Andrea said at last. "We Greeks have a word for what he feels—*kefi*, that indefinable exuberance of heart." She smiled. "He is not often home, and to have something of such consequence—both personal and business-wise—to celebrate . . ."

"Businesswise?" Helen questioned, confused.

"I'm sure Alexander has told you all about the international problems affecting our family's shipping interests," Andrea continued easily.

"No, he hasn't."

"But he told us that was one of the main reasons you two decided to marry so suddenly. I . . . I thought you knew all about Natasha."

"What . . . about Natasha?"

Andrea's eyes darkened with alarm. "I should never have brought her up, but I thought since you were living with her in Athens you were bound to know about . . . *everything.*"

"Of course I know that she and Alexander are good friends," Helen said quietly, a strange apprehension gripping her heart. "But what has she got to do with our marriage?"

"Well, she *is* the cause of my family's problems," Andrea said with uncustomary passion. "Ever since she left Russia, she's followed Alexander from place to place, trying to make him care for her. She even came here once. The newspapers have written many stories —lies that the two of them are having an affair. And does *she* care what it does to his business?"

Helen's voice was deadly quiet. "What does it do to his business, Andrea?"

"Well . . . because of the publicity, the Soviets think he helped Natasha defect. They're threatening to retaliate by closing their ports to his ships—which means that some of the firms leasing his ships do not wish to renew their leases. And other companies are reluctant to lease ships from him."

"Oh." The wind gusting up from the Aegean chilled her, numbing her senses, as though a layer of ice covered her skin.

"Helen, that's why my family and I were so thrilled when Alexander told us he was planning to marry you. My father has been begging him for months to take a decent bride and put an end to these rumors."

The two women continued their walk, and Helen somehow forced mechanical answers whenever they were necessary.

So . . . theirs was a marriage of convenience. Alexander was merely using her as a cover for his sordid relationship with Natasha. No wonder now that the wedding ceremony had been performed, he preferred the company of his friends to her.

Helen realized suddenly why Alexander had wanted her to live with him, why he had had her act as his hostess the evening he'd entertained the Soviets. He had been attempting to create the impression that he was interested in her and not Natasha—but only for business reasons. No wonder he had never seduced her. He had never . . . really . . . wanted her—at least no more than he wanted any woman.

When Andrea suggested they return to the party, Helen said she wanted to go to her room to freshen up first. Once inside her bedroom, Helen collapsed onto an overstuffed chair.

He had never . . . really . . . wanted her; yet, because of his business, he had married her. Her heart pounded unsteadily. Why had she married him? Fool! Why? He was a cad! Worse even than Hal! If only she weren't trapped on this island of his. If only she could run away and be free of him and this heartbreak that was tearing her to pieces! Her whole body quivered, but no tears fell. At last she wearily undressed and crawled into bed.

The music continued into the night and she tossed, burying her head in her pillow trying to blot out the sound of it because it made her think of him. When an hour passed and he did not come, she felt strangely disappointed and then furious at herself because she wanted him—in spite of everything.

She was still awake when the door was opened slowly. She squeezed her eyes tightly shut against the ray of light illuminating her face. Her pulse raced. Knowing that he was studying her features, she scarcely dared to breathe. Then the door closed, and thinking he'd gone, her eyes flew open.

To her horror, Alexander, his black coat slung carelessly across one shoulder, was staring down at her, a knowing look in his bold, dark eyes. She snapped her eyelids shut once more.

"That act wouldn't have tricked a child," he said, sardonic mockery coating his words. "I missed you at the party. Are you ill?" When she did not answer, he said, "I'm beginning to think this is only a case of bridal jitters." He knelt on the bed and leaned over her, reaching for her hand, which she pulled quickly away.

"Leave me alone," she muttered bitterly, aware of a treacherous weakness stirring inside her because of his nearness.

"Tonight you are my wife," he said, dismissing her command as though it were of no more importance than the utterance of a child.

Trembling, she watched him strip off his shirt and toss it onto a nearby chair. Then he loomed over her—lean and dark, devastatingly virile.

Hadn't he used her enough? Did he have to use her physically, as well? A helpless sob caught and spasmed in her throat. She had to find a way to stop him.

"Alexander, our marriage was a mistake," she said in a small, quavering voice. "I don't want to be your wife. I don't want . . . you." She tried to wriggle free of the covers and escape him.

His black eyes flashed with angry determination as he caught her by the waist and pulled her hard against himself. He was warm like a raging fire, and the heat of him seemed to blaze through her like a conflagration.

"Don't you?" he muttered hoarsely against her lips, before his mouth claimed hers, muffling her response. The tight circle of his arms crushed her against him in a passionate embrace that seemed to fuse their bodies into one. Then slowly he lowered her to the bed and followed her down.

His fierce desire swept her defenses away, all thought, all anger from her mind, and in their place was only a keen awareness of him as a man. She felt vividly alive. Her pulse rate quickened. And when she moved her lips in reply to his kiss, and arched her body against his, his own desire heightened.

"Do you want me to stop . . . now, Helen?" he asked huskily, as he pressed his mouth into the silky, flowing waves of her hair.

She drew in a ragged breath, hating herself, and him, as well, because he could so effortlessly arouse this aching, all-consuming need she had for him.

His warm lips, moving aginst her scalp, hesitated. "Do you?" he demanded, pulling away from her.

Her heart gave a sudden lurch. She couldn't bear for him to leave her. A sighing protest escaped her lips.

Her hands reached around his neck, and gently in answer to his question, she pulled his face down to hers, kissing his roughened cheek, his throat, his mouth.

Then they were lost in a violent whirlpool of emotion —each aware only of the pleasurable need that only the other could quench.

Afterward, they lay together in one another's arms— deeply contented.

She had pleased him, and slowly, carefully, the second time, he took the time to please her.

He said words to her in Greek, love words, and then he taught her to say them back to him. And he laughed low, nuzzling against her throat, when she spoke them, as though he were amused by her stumbling attempts.

His kisses grew more intense, his embrace more intimate. She felt strange, exquisite sensations as he drew her, unresisting, to new heights of dizzying passion. And . . . later . . . they slept deeply.

The loft was alight with streaming sunlight as Helen awakened and pushed the satin coverlets to the edge of the bed. Drowsily, she reached for Alexander, only to discover a vast, cold emptiness where he had lain. His absence was vaguely upsetting.

Of course she'd known last night when they'd arrived in Athens that the honeymoon was over. They'd had one marvelous week of island-hopping in the Aegean, of spending whole afternoons making love, of thrilling to each new discovery they made about each other, of awakening in one another's arms, of countless other new delights. And during those idyllic days and nights, all of her doubts about him had been pressed to the back of her mind.

And now—this morning—he'd left for work without

even a good-bye kiss. Was his business so important to him? And remembering Andrea's words—spoken on her wedding day—the question hung in her mind like an ominous cloud.

She dressed hurriedly and went down to breakfast. Natasha, clad in a white leotard and tights, was waiting for her. Although she looked lovely with her raven hair coiled on top of her head, the harsh morning sunlight was unkind, and Helen realized for the first time that the dancer was much older than she had believed.

"I had breakfast with Alexis," Natasha said triumphantly, fine lines crinkling beneath her eyes as she smiled. "I must say, he was certainly in a hurry to get off to work." She took a long swallow of coffee; her green eyes above the china coffee cup were smugly feline.

"His work piled up . . . while he was gone." With shaking fingers, Helen poured herself some tea.

"Is that it—really?" Natasha queried maliciously.

"What are you implying?"

"That if he shared the bed of a woman instead of an ignorant child, he wouldn't have been so eager to leave. Alexis is a sophisticated man. You will not hold him long."

Stiffening, Helen drew in a deep, long breath. She realized her own doubts about Alexander made her doubly vulnerable to Natasha's gibes. "I have no intention of listening to this," Helen replied quietly, turning on her heel to depart.

"I'm beginning to believe you *were* telling the truth before—when you said you weren't sleeping with Alexis. Poor darling! It must have been very frustrating for him. A unique experience. Still, I'm sure you realize the only reason he married you was because of . . . me."

173

Natasha's voice was fading as Helen walked briskly away, but the dancer's words engraved themselves indelibly in Helen's mind.

She still felt shattered an hour later when Alexander called.

"Is something wrong, Helen?"

"Alexander . . ." She paused. "I-I'm missing you," she admitted weakly, feeling terribly gladdened by the concern she detected in his deep voice.

"Me, too, darling, but I'm afraid that's going to get worse before it gets better. That's why I called. Something's come up, and I'm leaving for Paris in an hour."

"What? W-will you be back . . . tonight?"

"I'm afraid not."

"Oh."

"I'd take you with me, but this is going to be a quick trip—all business. I wouldn't have any time alone with you if you came."

"Of course." She swallowed at the lump of disappointment lodged squarely in her throat.

"I'll call you from Paris," he promised gently, and then he was gone.

She felt desolate. Natasha's taunts magnified in importance. *He only married me because of her. He only married me because of her.* The words tumbled around and around in her brain, until she squeezed her hands against either temple. She mustn't—she simply mustn't—let herself believe that.

I-I have to trust him, she told herself desperately. *I love him. He's not like Hal.* But Andrea had said he'd married for business reasons, and Alexander had never once mentioned any of his business problems. Was that because he wished to conceal from her why he had married her? Not once had he spoken of love. And this omission struck her as significant. Suddenly, she was remembering Hal and his too-frequent business trips,

174

his glib excuses, and her mother's unwarranted trust in him.

He's not like Hal! He's not! He'd been so kind to Gary. And . . . yet her painful doubts remained.

After lunch she discovered Eloise, one of the dancers, in the theater by herself. Eloise was Helen's favorite friend from the company.

"Where is everyone else?" Helen asked. "I thought a rehearsal was scheduled for this afternoon." Her words were hollow sounds echoing in the hushed theater.

"Natasha canceled it—just like that!" Eloise snapped her fingers theatrically in a gesture that mimicked Natasha's airy movements.

In spite of a gnawing fear, a smile wavered on Helen's lips. Natasha's arrogance was hard for many of the other dancers to endure. "But why?"

"I think she said . . . yes, I'm sure of it—she was going to Paris. It must be a quick trip, though. We have another rehearsal scheduled for tomorrow afternoon." Eloise packed her dancing slippers into the valise beside her. "Hey, you all right? You don't look at all well. You're as white as that wall."

"I-I'm fine," Helen returned shakily.

Eloise snapped the locks of her valise. "Well, see you tomorrow. I'm off to the beach." She waved, and Helen was only vaguely aware of gold-trimmed doors closing softly behind her. Her legs went limp at the knees, and she grabbed for the back of one of the theater seats and held onto it for support.

Natasha . . . Paris . . . Alexander . . . This didn't have to mean that Natasha was going to Paris to be with him.

But . . . somehow . . . she knew that it did.

Chapter Eleven

Breakfast alone—it was becoming her habit, Helen thought dismally as she seated herself on the terrace. Gary had returned to Marianatos to visit Andrea again. As Helen unfolded the English newspaper Alexander had subscribed to for her, Maria poured her a cup of steaming coffee.

Black script blurred. Helen was incapable of concentration. She hadn't slept the night before. All she could think of us was Alexander and Natasha. Were they . . . together?

Idly sipping her coffee and turning the pages, she waited for Maria to bring her breakfast. Then suddenly as she flipped to a page in the society section, her heart jumped to her throat. She let out a strangled cry. The fragile china cup she'd been holding with one hand shattered onto the flagstones, and she scarcely noticed the scalding liquid splashing against her ankles. The long, graceful fingers of her other hand curled savagely against the page, crumpling the newsprint.

Wrapped in Alexander's arms, Natasha smiled mockingly from the center of the page. Alexander's own hard expression was inscrutable. Her eyes brimming, Helen stared into the newsprint-blackness of his gaze. *Why?* her lips questioned soundlessly. Even his photograph tugged at her senses, reminding her too forcefully of his masculine virility, his unrelenting strength. She dragged her eyes from his picture to the article beneath it, and each word seared her soul like a red-hot iron. "Recently married entrepreneur Alexander Marianatos dining at Maxim's with ex-girl friend, famed ballerina Natasha Chernitzky . . ."

Unable to read further because the black letters were swimming, Helen swallowed hard against the bitter aftertaste of her coffee.

Her chin tilting proudly back, Helen forced herself to stand up on legs that miraculously supported her. She felt slightly nauseated. There was no point in her waiting for Maria to bring her tray. She wouldn't be able to eat a bite.

Her slow, purposeful walk to the library concealed the fact that inside she felt like she was flying into a million pieces. She dialed the first airline listed in the telephone directory. Three wrong numbers later an airline recording answered and put her on hold for an interminable five minutes.

There were no direct flights to New York available. "But Miss, you'll have a twelve-hour layover in London if you take that flight," the girl on the other end of the telephone warned.

"Just book me—today—on any plane leaving Athens," Helen said listlessly. "I don't care." Nothing mattered—except getting away before Alexander returned.

A vision of him—bronzed from their week in the Aegean—haunted her, causing a slow ache to move through her.

She never wanted to see him again, and yet she yearned for him. Of course, the man she really wanted didn't exist, she told herself. That photograph had confirmed all her doubts and crushed all her hopes for their future. Her heart wasn't broken; it was shattered —like a crystal vase smashed into irreparable bits.

She was not going to end up like her mother! She had already foolishly allowed herself to fall in love with a man incapable of loving only one woman. But she was not going to spend a lifetime letting him hurt her. That would only compound her initial mistake.

Knitting her brows together, she tried to read what she'd scribbled about her departure time. What had that girl said—exactly? Helen's mind was a maze of tangled times and flight numbers. At last she deciphered her blue ballpoint scrawl. Normally, her handwriting was precise and clearly legible.

Her flight was scheduled for six P.M., which gave her several hours to pack.

While Helen was stuffing necessities into her suitcases, Maria signaled her on the intercom that there was a telephone call for her.

She couldn't talk! Not to anyone! A turbulent shudder wracked her. But she had to. She had to preserve the façade of normalcy until she was safely gone. She smoothed her hair back behind her ears, and sighed heavily in a vain attempt to calm herself. Then she fumbled for the receiver.

"Helen . . ." Alexander's deep voice seared through her with unexpected violence like a blaze of lightning hitting its target. She gasped; then fear paralyzed her throat muscles, emprisoning the gulp of air she'd breathed. The insincere warmth of his voice was torture. Somehow, she forced out the air bubble, almost strangling.

"I worked half the night," he said, "and was able to complete almost all my business. I have one more appointment. Then I'll be home tonight—a little before eight." He sounded very, very happy. When she made no response, Alexander asked, "Helen, is anything wrong?"

"N-no. . . ." Her voice lied with a smoothness she was far from feeling, and he seemed satisfied. Coolly, she asked, "You worked *all night* . . . without even breaking for dinner?"

She caught his faint hesitation before he spoke. "I would have skipped dinner if it had been up to me. But Harold Cameron had reservations at Maxim's, so I went with him. Actually, the wine put Harold into such a good mood that he agreed to all my terms much more readily than I'd anticipated. That's one of the reasons I'll be able to get home . . . to you . . . tonight." The suggestive hint in his husky voice evoked a quivering response which maddened her, and she almost slammed the receiver down onto the hook.

How could lies roll off his tongue so effortlessly? Experience—she told herself.

When he hung up, she collapsed into a huddle on the floor. His call had unnerved her. As always, he seemed to care, and she foolishly wanted to believe him—even his lie about eating with Harold. Perhaps there was a half-truth somewhere in that story. But pictures didn't lie! And husbands determined to cheat on their wives did!

If she stayed, their every encounter would be like this—clever insincerities on his part countered by her own foolish desire to believe him. She couldn't stay with him without growing to despise both herself and him.

And yet . . . without him . . . her life stretched before her like the bleak emptiness of a desert landscape.

Helen carried her suitcases downstairs and was going to look for Georgios when she heard the strains of *The Firebird Suite* coming from the theater. It was two o'clock—time for the dress rehearsal. The ballet was to be performed the next night for the public.

Curious to know if Natasha had returned, Helen slipped soundlessly into a back seat of the theater and allowed the mysterious music to envelop her. The weeks seemed to slip away, carrying her back to Paris and that first night when she'd gone to the ballet and then . . . afterward met Alexander.

The stage, which had been shrouded in darkness, brightened slightly. Ivan, clad as a Russian peasant, danced in a fantastic forest. Suddenly the music whirred rapidly and playful amber light began to chase him. Frightened, he ran and hid. The music increased in speed, and suddenly the dazzling firebird flew about the stage in a series of expertly executed leaps and poses.

Natasha danced brilliantly—triumphantly, it seemed to Helen. The stage was ablaze with the light of many torches. And from a distance the ballerina's exquisite grace made her appear much younger than she was.

Helen could bear no more. She understood too well the reason behind Natasha's savage brilliance.

Deciding to escape at once to the airport, Helen tiptoed from the theater, shutting the doors against the forceful music.

Her two suitcases stood in the foyer, but her purse was missing. How could she have forgotten to bring it down? She chastised herself. A shiver of fear traced through her, and she knew she was overreacting because she was already so upset. Still, her purse was the only thing she had to have, for it contained her passport and money.

Desperately, she wanted to get away from this house and everything that reminded her of Alexander. Her disrupted emotions magnified any obstacle toward reaching that goal. What if she couldn't find her purse—in time?

She forced herself to try to remember where she'd last seen it. The bedside table where she'd left a note for Alexander and Gary sprang instantly to her mind. Inserting her key into the elevator, she stepped inside quickly when the doors opened. The elevator creaked and hesitated halfway up, increasing her feelings of apprehension. Slowly, the ascent was completed.

Her purse was not on the beside table! Nor could she find it immediately. Nervously, she darted about the loft looking for it, her anxiety compounding as each minute ticked by. At last, after a thirty-minute search, she discovered it wedged between the bed and the bedside table. She heaved a breathless sigh of relief as she glanced at her watch. It was only three o'clock. The airport was just over an hour's drive from the house, which left her with time to spare.

But when she put her key into the elevator, nothing happened. Her empty stomach lurched. Refusing to believe the obvious, she jiggled the key frantically in the lock. Still nothing. Her heartbeat skittered. The elevator had never malfunctioned before! She must be doing something wrong. Oh, why wasn't she more mechanical—like Gary?

Taking her key out, she repeated the process with the same results. She wiped at the perspiration now dotting her brow. It was so hot! Unaccountably hot! Apparently, the air conditioning was out, as well as the elevator.

The acrid scent of something electrical burning arrested her attention, causing a tremor to jerk through her. Jingling keys fell to the floor with a thud. Then all was silence. She strained to hear the music from beneath, but to her horror she heard none.

The Firebird. Fire . . . the torches . . . Her mind

leaped from thought to thought. Natasha's blazing version of the ballet was very dramatic, and yet unbidden, the memory of that accidental fire in Paris returned. Had there been another accident? Was the house on fire? The idea was preposterous!

Threads of smoke seeped through the air-conditioning vents and through the elevator doors, confirming her worst fears. The loft was directly over the stage, and no one even knew she was up here!

The smoke was rapidly thickening. Choking, she made her way to the balcony outside. Alexander had said it was made of stone. She could see dense clouds of whirling fumes and sparks racing up the sides of the theater. She groped her way along the balustrade until she found the ladder that scaled the stone side of the building. But as she looked over the edge, the grounds beneath rippled in the heat waves. Clutching the stone railing, she tried to bring specific objects into focus. But the old familiar dizzying sensation was sweeping over her as her fear of heights possessed her. The fluid rectangle that was the pool lost shape and blurred. Her vision blackened—like a scrap of paper afire, around the edges first. Her strength seemed to flow out of her. There was no way she could climb down that ladder.

Black smoke billowed from the glass door she'd left partially opened. Dimly, she heard the screaming of sirens, and more faintly the sound of someone calling her name.

The heat, the smoke, her fear combined, suffocating her. She couldn't breathe. The stone beneath her feet seemed to sway, and her grip on the balustrade weakened. But ironically the only thing that mattered to her in that last moment of consciousness was Alexander and the fact that she would never see him again. Faintly, she murmured his name many times before she surrendered to the tide of darkness curling over her.

"Alexander . . ." Helen twisted as though even his name brought pain. He would not come. He was away—lost to her forever. There was Natasha. . . . But still she called to him, again and again.

"I'm here, little one." The lazy drawl was a slurred, indistinct sound, caressing her, and she held onto it.

"Alexander . . ."

"Yes, my darling. You're safe now . . . with me. Don't try to talk. You must rest."

She felt the incredible warmth of him cradling her close against himself; the brush of his lips—feather-soft upon her forehead. She heard the erratic tone of his heart pounding beneath his hard chest, and she snuggled closer, drawing security from his nearness. Her fingers traced the jagged edges of a heavy sliver of metal before she realized without seeing it that it was the medallion he always wore—the bird of fire. She gripped it tightly, like catching hold of a lifeline.

He was here! This was real! Her lashes fluttered open, revealing his soot-blackened, harsh features to her clearly. There was an ugly, scarlet stain above one of his slashing brows.

They were lying beneath the satin coverlet of her bed in her old room.

"W-what happened?" she asked hesitantly. "The loft and theater . . ."

". . . can be rebuilt—this time out of stone," he finished as though they mattered little. "The rest of the house is undamaged."

She touched the sticky moisture above his eye, and when he winced she said tenderly, "You've been hurt."

"It's only a scratch." His intent gaze was magnetic. "I almost lost you, my darling." She felt the muscled

183

strength of his arms about her, the warm imprint of his body against her own. "You fainted, and I had to carry you down. I was almost . . . too late." He bit out the last savagely, as though had that been the case, he would have never forgiven himself.

The loft had been an inferno and he'd come up and saved her—risking his own life.

"You could have been killed!" she gasped, the horror of that reality all-consuming.

"Do you think I would want to live—without you?" he demanded, the ardor in his deep voice, as well as the fierce gleam in his black eyes, underscoring the depth of the emotion he felt for her.

"But Natasha . . . I thought you married me because of your business. . . ."

"When are you going to stop attributing an ulterior motive to my every action?" he said, his voice roughening, although he tried to suppress his impatience. "I married you for one reason only—because I love you. You're the only woman I want. What do I have to do to prove to you that I'm not like your father? Because I'm fresh out of ideas."

"H-how did you know about Hal?"

"I thought it was very odd when he didn't take the time to come to our wedding. When I asked Gary about him, he told me enough so that I began to wonder if you weren't transferring your lack of trust in Hal to me."

"You are handsome and charming like him."

"And for those crimes you condemn me like a criminal," he mocked. "Would you prefer a husband who was ugly and sadistic?"

"Of course not," she whispered, knowing he was the only man she could ever love. "But . . . what about Natasha? She was in Paris . . . with you."

"She was in Paris . . . but *not* with me."

"I-I saw your picture in the paper . . . together . . . in Maxim's."

"Harold showed me a copy of that paper right after I talked to you this morning, and I realized you'd probably seen it over breakfast. That's why I chartered a plane and flew home early—to explain. There were four other businessmen at the table with us. The photographer clevery failed to include them. I can give you their names and phone numbers. . . ."

"That won't be necessary," she murmured, ecstasy winging through her because she saw the truth in every line of his strong features.

"Natasha only dropped by our table to celebrate the fact she'd just been offered the lead in a new ballet. At her age, such parts aren't always easily obtained."

"Oh."

"When are you going to believe in yourself and realize what a lovely person you are? I love you. I think I fell in love with you the first night I met you. But you were so set against me, so determined to leave Greece and me. But when you came to my office—because of Gary—I decided I couldn't let you go. I wanted you so desperately I forced you to live with me, hoping you would realize I wasn't the ogre you kept accusing me of being. But things seemed to get worse for a while. Even after we married, I knew you still doubted me."

"But you never . . . told me before that you loved me."

"Would you have believed me?"

"Probably not," she admitted.

"I wish there was some way I could convince you I truly love you and only you," he muttered hoarsely.

She ran her fingers through his thick, tumbling hair and drew his head down so that his sensual mouth hovered above hers. "I think you're smart enough to find a way," she said, arching her body against his.

His lips quirked before curving into a knowing grin. "Why . . . you impudent little tease," he groaned, pulling her closer.

"I'm not . . . teasing," she returned huskily, mesmerized by his intense gaze.

"You'd better not be," he whispered fiercely before his lips lowered to hers, lingering, tantalizing, sending molten waves of desire pulsing through her arteries as though his very touch was fire.

Satin rustled as he pressed her backward upon the bed, and the sheer intensity of his passion silenced her doubts about his love forever.

Silhouette **Romance**

15-Day Free Trial Offer
6 Silhouette Romances

6 Silhouette Romances, free for 15 days! We'll send you 6 new Silhouette Romances to keep for 15 days, absolutely free! If you decide not to keep them, send them back to us. You pay nothing.

Free Home Delivery. But if you enjoy them as much as we think you will, keep them by paying the invoice enclosed with your free trial shipment. We'll pay all shipping and handling charges. You get the convenience of Home Delivery and we pay the postage and handling charge each month.

Don't miss a copy. The Silhouette Book Club is the way to make sure you'll be able to receive every new romance we publish before they're sold out. There is no minimum number of books to buy and you can cancel at any time.

This offer expires October 31, 1982

IT'S YOUR OWN SPECIAL TIME

Contemporary romances for today's women.
Each month, six very special love stories will be yours
from SILHOUETTE. Look for them wherever books are sold
or order now from the coupon below.

$1.50 each

Hampson	☐ 1	☐ 4	☐ 16	☐ 27	Browning	☐ 12	☐ 38	☐ 53	☐ 73
	☐ 28	☐ 40	☐ 52	☐ 64	☐ 94		☐ 93			
Stanford	☐ 6	☐ 25	☐ 35	☐ 46	Michaels	☐ 15	☐ 32	☐ 61	☐ 87
	☐ 58	☐ 88			John	☐ 17	☐ 34	☐ 57	☐ 85
Hastings	☐ 13	☐ 26	☐ 44	☐ 67	Beckman	☐ 8	☐ 37	☐ 54	☐ 72
Vitek	☐ 33	☐ 47	☐ 66	☐ 84		☐ 96			

$1.50 each

☐ 5 Goforth	☐ 29 Wildman	☐ 56 Trent	☐ 79 Halldorson
☐ 7 Lewis	☐ 30 Dixon	☐ 59 Vernon	☐ 80 Stephens
☐ 9 Wilson	☐ 31 Halldorson	☐ 60 Hill	☐ 81 Roberts
☐ 10 Caine	☐ 36 McKay	☐ 62 Hallston	☐ 82 Dailey
☐ 11 Vernon	☐ 39 Sinclair	☐ 63 Brent	☐ 83 Halston
☐ 14 Oliver	☐ 41 Owen	☐ 69 St. George	☐ 86 Adams
☐ 19 Thornton	☐ 42 Powers	☐ 70 Afton Bonds	☐ 89 James
☐ 20 Fulford	☐ 43 Robb	☐ 71 Ripy	☐ 90 Major
☐ 21 Richards	☐ 45 Carroll	☐ 74 Trent	☐ 92 McKay
☐ 22 Stephens	☐ 48 Wildman	☐ 75 Carroll	☐ 95 Wisdom
☐ 23 Edwards	☐ 49 Wisdom	☐ 76 Hardy	☐ 97 Clay
☐ 24 Healy	☐ 50 Scott	☐ 77 Cork	☐ 98 St. George
	☐ 55 Ladame	☐ 78 Oliver	☐ 99 Camp

$1.75 each

☐ 100 Stanford	☐ 105 Eden	☐ 110 Trent	☐ 115 John
☐ 101 Hardy	☐ 106 Dailey	☐ 111 South	☐ 116 Lindley
☐ 102 Hastings	☐ 107 Bright	☐ 112 Stanford	☐ 117 Scott
☐ 103 Cork	☐ 108 Hampson	☐ 113 Browning	☐ 118 Dailey
☐ 104 Vitek	☐ 109 Vernon	☐ 114 Michaels	☐ 119 Hampson

Silhouette Desire
15-Day Trial Offer

A new romance series
that explores
contemporary relationships
in exciting detail

Four Silhouette Desire romances, free for 15 days!
We'll send you four new Silhouette Desire romances
to look over for 15 days, absolutely free! If you decide
not to keep the books, return them and owe nothing.

Four books a month, free home delivery. If you like
Silhouette Desire romances as much as we think you
will, keep them and return your payment with the
invoice. Then we will send you four new books every
month to preview, just as soon as they are published.
You pay only for the books you decide to keep, and
you never pay postage and handling.

READERS' COMMENTS ON SILHOUETTE ROMANCES:

"I would like to congratulate you on the most wonderful books I've had the pleasure of reading. They are a tremendous joy to those of us who have yet to meet the man of our dreams. From reading your books I quite truly believe that he will some-day appear before me like a prince!"

—L.L.*, Hollandale, MS

"Your books are great, wholesome fiction, always with an upbeat, happy ending. Thank you."

—M.D., Massena, NY

"My boyfriend always teases me about Silhouette Books. He asks me, how's my love life and natu-rally I say terrific, but I tell him that there is always room for a little more romance from Sil-houette."

—F.N., Ontario, Canada

"I would like to sincerely express my gratitude to you and your staff for bringing the pleasure of your publications to my attention. Your books are well written, mature and very contemporary."

—D.D., Staten Island, NY

*names available on request

Silhouette Romance

Coming next month from
Silhouette Romances

Daring Encounter by Patti Beckman

Glamour, daring, mystique . . . Lord Richard Templeton had them all. And it was up to Andria to make America's top race idol an offer he couldn't refuse.

Devotion by Anne Hampson

Caryl's harmless masquerade backfired when Brad proposed to the wrong girl! Could she ever reveal herself and win his heart for her own?

Time Remembered by Lee Sawyer

His family had sent her father into bankruptcy years ago. But Sabrina couldn't deny the passion that engulfed her when Jules took her into his arms.

Game of Chance by Donna Vitek

Jason was everything Kit had ever hoped for, except that he was a gambler. Could she accept his profession, or would she lose the gamble—and his love?

An Ocean Of Love by Elizabeth Reynolds

He called her a gold digger and a fraud! Then suddenly, his attitude changed, and Jill found herself passionately in love with a man she didn't even like.

Yesterday's Bride by Susan Tracy

After years of separation, Leigh wanted to avoid seeing Jason again. But he lured her into his turbulent world, for she was his *wife!*

**Look for *Search For Love* by Nora Roberts
Available in July.**